# Introduction

# A: Legal and management

# B: Health and welfare

# C: General safety

# D: High risk activities

# E: Environment

# Contents

## F: Specialist activities

If you are preparing for a specialist test you also need to revise the appropriate specialist activity, from those listed below.

## Further information

# Introduction

## Contents

# Foreword

Construction is an exciting industry. There is constant change as work progresses to completion. We all recognise that a healthy and safe workforce is critical to the success of the industry, and it is essential that standards are not compromised.

Sadly, each year the construction industry accounts for more than a quarter of the UK's work-related fatal accidents. Over 4,500 workers die from the long-term effects of breathing in hazardous construction dusts and there are more than 1,900 specified injuries.

Many of these can be avoided by improving workers' hazard and risk awareness, through effective leadership and worker involvement, by providing the right tools and equipment, and a continued commitment to a fully trained and competent workforce.

The CITB *Health, safety and environment test* plays an important role in helping to achieve this. The test is a key part of obtaining a card, which provides proof that individuals working on construction sites have the required training and qualifications. The test continues to be a vital tool in helping the industry to improve its health, safety and environmental standards.

To this end, we have been consulting with industry and have refreshed the question bank and introduced the behavioural case studies based on the core principles of the industry's free film *Setting out*. The film explores what employers and sites must do for workers, and how workers need to behave and react to constantly changing site conditions. The question bank has also been reviewed to reflect the revised Construction (Design and Management) Regulations.

A dedicated set of respiratory risk questions is included to help improve awareness and to promote the necessary controls. It is widely recognised that management of health risks by industry has not improved at the same rate as improvements in the management of safety risks.

Managing the environment goes hand in hand with health and safety. Therefore, working in partnership with industry and the Green Construction Board, new questions have been introduced to help everyone understand some basic environmental responsibilities.

CITB is committed to continual improvement of delivery methods for specialist training and qualifications. We are constantly working on behalf of the industry, with the Government, Environment Agency and the HSE to drive forward improved standards.

If we all work together to support a workforce with the necessary skills, knowledge, training and experience we can have a huge impact on our industry – making it a safer and healthier place to work.

James Wates CBE
Chairman
CITB

# About the test

The CITB *Health, safety and environment test* helps raise standards across the industry. It ensures that workers meet a minimum level of health, safety and environmental awareness before going on site. It should be used as a stepping stone, encouraging employers and their workforce to go on and develop their knowledge even further.

## What has changed in the new Health, safety and environment test?

The test has been running for over 14 years and it underwent significant improvements in 2012. The improvements included an enhanced test and a new delivery infrastructure.

New content has been introduced for the 2015 edition including:

☑ new knowledge questions on Construction (Design and Management) Regulations 2015

☑ revisions to the environment questions.

## How is the test structured?

All tests last for 45 minutes and have 50 multiple-choice questions including:

☑ 12 behavioural case study questions about how you should behave on a construction site to stay healthy and safe, followed by 38 knowledge questions to check your knowledge of health, safety and environment issues.

☑ Different tests have been developed to meet the demands of different trades and professions. You will need to make sure that you take the right one.

The following tests are available:

☑ operative test

☑ specialist tests

☑ managers and professionals test.

## What are the knowledge questions?

The knowledge questions cover 16 core areas (presented in Sections A-E of this book) that are included in all the tests. These questions are very factual. For example they will ask you to identify fire extinguishers and signs. There is an additional knowledge question bank for each specialist test.

You will not need a detailed knowledge of the exact content or working of any regulations. However, you will need to show that you know what is required of you, the things you must do (or not do), and what to do in certain circumstances (for example, discovering an accident).

Many of the questions refer to the duties of employers. In law, the self-employed can have the same legal responsibilities as employers. To keep the questions as brief as possible, the content only refers to the duties of employers but the questions apply to both.

The questions are based on British legislation. However, Northern Ireland legislation differs from that in the rest of the UK. For practical reasons, all candidates (including those in Northern Ireland) will be tested on questions using legislation relevant to the rest of the UK only.

## What is a multiple-choice question?

The test is made up of multiple-choice questions. This means you will need to select the answer you think is correct from a set of possible answers.

Most questions will ask you to select a single answer. However, some of the knowledge questions will ask you to select multiple answers. This will always be clearly stated in the question.

## What are the behavioural case study questions?

The behavioural case study questions are designed to test how you respond to health and safety situations on a construction site. They are based on the principles established in the film *Setting out – what you should expect from a site and what they expect from you.*

Further information on the film and the transcript is provided at the back of this book.

Every test includes three case studies, each of which has four linked multiple-choice questions. These progress through a fictional situation faced by an individual working in the construction industry.

## What specialist tests are there?

A specialist test includes six questions from the appropriate specialist knowledge question bank (presented in Section F of this book), plus a selection of 32 core knowledge questions (presented in Sections A-E of this book).

There are currently 11 different specialist tests available including supervisory; demolition; highway works; specialist work at height; lifts and escalators; tunnelling; heating, ventilation, air conditioning and refrigeration (HVACR).

## Who writes the questions?

The question bank is developed by CITB with industry-recognised organisations which sit on or support the Health, safety and environment test question sub-committee. A full list of those parties that support the test is set out in the acknowledgements at the back of the book.

## Will the questions change?

Health, safety and environment legislation, regulations and best practice will change from time to time, but CITB makes every effort to keep the test and the revision material up to date.

- You will not be tested on questions that are deemed to no longer be appropriate.
- You will be tested on knowledge questions presented in the most up to date edition of the book. To revise effectively for the test you should use the latest edition. You can check which edition of the book you have at www.citb.co.uk/hsandetestupdate or phone 0344 994 4488.

# Preparing for a test

There are a number of ways you can prepare for your test.

| | Operatives | Specialists | Supervisors | Managers |
|---|---|---|---|---|
| Watch *Setting out* | Free to view at *www.citb.co.uk/settingout* | | | |
| Read the question and answer books | *HS&E test for operatives and specialists* (GT 100) | | | *HS&E test for managers and professionals –* (GT 200) |
| Use the digital products | *HS&E test for operatives and specialists* – *DVD* (GT 100 DVD) – *Download* (GT 100 DL) – *Apps* | | | *HS&E test for managers and professionals* – *DVD* (GT 200 DVD) – *Download* (GT 200 DL) – *Apps* |
| Read supporting knowledge material | *Safe start* (GE 707) | *Safe start* (GE 707) plus sector recommended supporting material | *Site supervision simplified* (GE 706) | *Construction site safety* (GE 700) |
| Complete an appropriate training course | Site Safety Plus – one-day Health and safety awareness course | Contact your industry body for recommendations | Site Safety Plus – two-day Site supervisor's safety training scheme | Site Safety Plus – five-day Site management safety training scheme |

## How can I increase my chances of success?

☑ Prepare using the recommended revision materials, working through all the knowledge questions.

☑ Watch the *Setting out* film to prepare for the behavioural case study questions.

☑ Complete a recommended training course.

☑ Book your test when you are confident with your topics and questions.

☑ Complete a timed simulated test a few days before (available on the DVD and download).

## What's on the DVD and downloads?

The DVD and downloads offer an interactive package that includes:

☑ the *Setting out* film and a sample behavioural case study

☑ all the knowledge questions and answers in both book and practice formats

☑ the real test tutorial

☑ a test simulator – all the functionality of the test with the real question bank

☑ voice-overs in English and Welsh for all questions.

The DVD also provides operative questions and *Setting out* with voice-overs in the following languages:

☑ Bulgarian       ☑ German       ☑ Polish       ☑ Romanian

☑ Czech           ☑ Hungarian    ☑ Portuguese   ☑ Russian

☑ French          ☑ Lithuanian   ☑ Punjabi      ☑ Spanish.

Please note: British Sign Language assistance is included on the GT 100 revision DVD and within the *Setting out* film.

## Where can I buy the revision material?

CITB has developed a range of revision material, including question and answer books, DVDs, downloads and a smartphone app that will help you to prepare for the test. For further information and to buy these products:

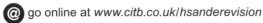 go online at *www.citb.co.uk/hsanderevision*

telephone 0344 994 4488
lines open Monday to Friday 8am to 8pm, and Saturday 8am to noon

visit a good bookshop, either in the high street or online for books and DVDs. Visit iTunes or Google Play for smartphone apps.

## Where can I find more information on your supporting publications?

CITB has developed a range of publications that present a detailed and comprehensive guide to the full range of topics covered in the test. They can be used to build awareness and understanding of the issues surrounding health and safety on a construction site. They provide the context for the questions that are asked.

The range of products includes: *Safe start* (GE 707), *Site supervision simplified* (GE 706) and *Construction site safety* (GE 700). For further information and to buy these products:

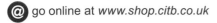 go online at *www.shop.citb.co.uk*

telephone 0344 994 4122
lines open Monday to Thursday 8.45am to 5pm and Friday 9am to 4pm.

## What is the Site Safety Plus Scheme?

CITB's Site Safety Plus Scheme is a comprehensive health and safety training programme designed to provide the building, civil engineering and allied industries with a range of courses for individuals seeking to develop their skill set in this area.

They are designed to give everyone from operative to senior manager the skill set they need to progress through the industry. From a one-day Health and safety awareness course to the five-day Site management safety training scheme (SMSTS), these courses will ensure that everyone benefits from the best possible training. For further information:

go online at *www.citb.co.uk/sitesafetyplus.*

## Booking a test

The easiest way to book your test is either online or by telephone. You will be given the date and time of your test immediately and offered the opportunity to buy revision material, such as books, DVDs, downloads and apps. You should be able to book a test at your preferred location within two weeks.

To book your test:

 go online at *www.citb.co.uk/hsandetest*

telephone 0344 994 4488
lines open Monday to Friday 8am to 8pm, and Saturday 8am to noon.

post in an application form (application forms are available from the website and the telephone number listed above).

When booking your test you will be able to choose whether to receive confirmation by email or by letter. It is important that you check the details (including the type of test, the location, the date and time) and follow any instructions it gives regarding the test.

You can also choose to receive an SMS text message or email reminder 24 hours before your test.

For those instances where a test is required at short notice it may be possible to turn up at a centre and take a test on the day (subject to available spaces). It's strongly advised that you do not rely on this option.

### What information do I need to book a test?

To book a test you should have the following information to hand.

- Which test you need to take.
- Whether you require any special assistance.
- Your chosen method of payment (debit or credit card details).
- Your address details.
- Your CITB registration number (you will have one of these if you have taken the test before, or applied for certain card schemes including CSCS, CPCS, CISRS, etc.).

### Where can I take a test?

To sit a *Health, safety and environment test* you will need to visit a CITB-approved test centre. There are three different types of centre.

- A fixed test centre operated by our delivery provider.
  To find your nearest test centre visit *www.citb.co.uk/hsandetest*. These test centres will be able to offer tests from Monday to Saturday, but local opening times will vary. Normal opening hours are Monday to Friday 8am to 8pm and Saturdays 8am to noon.
- An independent Internet Test Centre (for example as operated by a college, training provider or commercial organisation). Please contact these test centres directly for further information and to book a test.

- A corporate testing unit which can be established at a suitable venue for a group of candidates. For further information on this service there is a dedicated booking line 0344 994 4492.

## Is there any special assistance available when taking the test?

### Voice-over assistance

All tests can be booked with English or Welsh voice-overs.

### Foreign language assistance

- The operatives test can be booked with voice-overs in the following languages: Bulgarian, Czech, French, German, Hungarian, Lithuanian, Polish, Portuguese, Punjabi, Romanian, Russian, Spanish.

  An interpreter can be requested if assistance is required in other languages.

- The specialist tests can be booked with an interpreter but no pre-recorded voice-overs are available.

- The managers and professionals test does not allow foreign language assistance because a basic command of English or Welsh is required in order to sit the test.

### Sign language assistance

The operatives test can be booked with British Sign Language on screen. If you need assistance in the other tests a signer can be provided.

### Further assistance

If you need any other special assistance (such as a reader, signer, interpreter, or extra time) this can be provided but you will need to book through a dedicated booking line 0344 994 4491.

## What services are there for Welsh speakers?

- All tests can be booked with Welsh voice-overs.
- All revision DVDs include Welsh voice-overs.
- There is a dedicated Welsh booking line 0344 994 4490.

## How do I cancel or postpone my test?

To cancel or reschedule your test you should go online or call the booking number at least 72 hours (three working days) before your test. There will be no charge for cancelling or rescheduling the test online at www.citb.co.uk/testingservices outside of the 72 hour period. Reschedules and cancellations made via the telephone booking line will incur an administration fee.

## What if I do not receive a confirmation email or letter?

If you do not receive a confirmation email or letter within the time specified please call the booking line to check your booking has been made.

We cannot take responsibility for postal delays. If you miss your test event, you will unfortunately forfeit your fee.

## Taking a test

### Before the test

On the day of the test you will need to:

- allow plenty of time to get to the test centre and arrive at least 15 minutes before the start of the test
- take your confirmation email or letter
- take proof of identity that bears your photo and your signature (such as driving licence card or passport – please visit *www.citb.co.uk/hsandetest* for full list of acceptable documentation).

On arrival at the test centre, staff will check your documents to ensure you are booked onto the correct test. If you do not have all the relevant documents you will not be able to sit your test and you will lose your fee.

### During the test

The tests are all delivered on a computer screen. However, you do not need to be familiar with computers and the test does not involve any typing. All you need to do is click on the relevant answer boxes, using either a mouse or by touching the screen.

Before the test begins you can choose to work through a tutorial. It explains how the test works and lets you try out the buttons and functions that you will use while taking your test.

The test will contain 50 multiple-choice questions which you will need to complete in 45 minutes.

There will be information displayed on the screen which shows you how far you are through the test and how much time you have remaining.

### After the test

At the end of the test there is an optional survey that gives you the chance to provide feedback on the test process.

You will be provided with a printed score report after you have left the test room. This will tell you whether you have passed or failed your test, and give feedback on areas where further learning and revision is recommended.

### What do I do if I fail?

If you fail your test, your score report will provide feedback on areas where you got questions wrong.

It is strongly recommended that you revise these areas thoroughly before re-booking. You will have to wait at least 48 hours before you can take the test again.

## What do I do if I pass?

A *Health, safety and environment test* pass is often a necessary requirement when applying to join a construction industry card scheme. Different schemes exist in different trades and professions. Membership of a relevant scheme helps you prove that you can do your job, and that you can do it safely. Access to construction sites may require a relevant scheme card.

Once you have passed your test, you should, if you have not done so already, consider applying to join the relevant card scheme. However please be aware that you may need to complete further training, assessment and/or testing to meet their specific entry requirements.

To find out more about many of the recognised schemes:

@ go online at *www.citb.co.uk/cardschemes.*

| Further scheme contact details | | telephone | go online |
|---|---|---|---|
| General | Construction Skills Certification Scheme (CSCS) | 0344 994 4777 | www.cscs.uk.com |
| | Northern Ireland: Construction Skills Register (CSR) | 028 9087 7150 | www.cefni.co.uk |
| Plant operatives | Construction Plant Competence Scheme (CPCS) | 0844 815 7274 | www.citb.co.uk/cpcs |
| Demolition operatives | Certificate of Competence of Demolition Operatives (CCDO) | 0844 826 8385 | www.ndtg.org |
| Scaffolders | Construction Industry Scaffolders Record Scheme (CISRS) | 0844 815 7223 | www.cisrs.org.uk |
| HVACR | Engineering Services SKILLcard (ESS) | 01768 860 406 | www.skillcard.org.uk |

# Augmented reality

## What is augmented reality?

Augmented reality (AR) is cutting-edge technology. It provides layers of digital information (videos, photographs, sounds) simply by downloading an app and using the camera and sensors in your smartphone or tablet.

This technology has been used to connect you with additional and complementary content. This can be accessed via your mobile device when you install the Layar app.

## How do I install the Layar app?

- ☑ Go to the appropriate app store (Apple or Android) and download the Layar app (free of charge) to your mobile phone or tablet.
- ☑ Look out for this logo [right], which is on the cover of this book and indicates that you are on a Layar-friendly page.
- ☑ Open the Layar app and scan the Layar-friendly page.
- ☑ Wait for the page to activate on your device.
- ☑ Touch one of the buttons that have appeared to access additional content.

## Where can I find augmented reality in this publication?

The following content is accessible by scanning the cover page of this publication.

- ☑ Check for new or changed questions.
- ☑ Book a Health, safety and environment test.
- ☑ Watch the Setting out film.
- ☑ Watch a behavioural case studies film.
- ☑ Buy revision material.
- ☑ Buy the Health, safety and environment test revision app (Apple and Android).
- ☑ Buy supporting publications.

# A

# Legal and management

## Contents

## 01 General responsibilities

### 1.1

Who is responsible for reporting any unsafe conditions on site?

A The site manager

B The client

C Health and Safety Executive (HSE) inspectors

D Everyone on site

### 1.2

During site induction you do not understand something the presenter says. What should you do?

A Attend another site induction

B Ask the presenter to explain it again

C Guess what the presenter was trying to tell you

D Wait until the end then ask someone else to explain

### 1.3

What should you do if the safety rules given in your site induction seem out of date as work progresses?

A Do nothing, as you are not responsible for safety on site

B Speak to your supervisor about your concerns

C Speak to your workmates to see if they have any new rules

D Make up your own safety rules to suit the changing conditions

### 1.4

What is the most important reason for keeping your work area clean and tidy?

A To prevent slips, trips and falls

B So that you don't have to have a big clean-up at the end of the week

C So that waste skips can be emptied more often

D To recycle waste and help the environment

### 1.5

What should you do if the work of another contractor is affecting your safety?

A Stop work and go home

B Stop work and speak to your supervisor

C Stop work and speak to the contractor's supervisor

D Stop work and speak to the contractor who is doing the job

### 1.6

What does it mean if the equipment you are using is issued with a prohibition notice?

A You must not use it unless your supervisor is present

B You must not use it until it is made safe

C You can use it as long as you take more care

D Only supervisors can use it

Answers: 1.1 = D   1.2 = B   1.3 = B   1.4 = A   1.5 = B   1.6 = B

## 1.7

The whole site has been issued with a prohibition notice. What does this mean to you?

- A) You can carry on working because it was nothing to do with you
- B) You are not allowed to use any power tools
- C) You can finish what you are doing and then go home
- D) You must stop work because the site is unsafe

## 1.8

After watching you work, a Health and Safety Executive (HSE) inspector issues an improvement notice. What does this mean?

- A) You are not working fast enough
- B) You need to improve the standard of your work
- C) You are not working in a safe way
- D) The way you are working has improved since the last time they saw you

## 1.9

Who has legal duties under the Health and Safety at Work Act?

- A) Just employers
- B) Just operatives
- C) All people at work
- D) Just self-employed people

## 1.10

Why is the Health and Safety at Work Act important to you as a worker? Give **two** answers.

- A) It tells you which parts of the site are dangerous
- B) It must be learned before starting work
- C) It puts legal duties on your employer to provide a safe place to work
- D) It tells you how to do your job
- E) It puts legal duties on you as a worker

**A 01**

## 1.11

Which of these is **not** your legal duty as a worker?

- A) To look after your own health and safety
- B) To look after the health and safety of anyone else who might be affected by your work
- C) To write your own risk assessments
- D) Not to interfere with anything provided for health and safety

## 1.12

Who is responsible for managing health and safety on construction sites?

- A) The company safety officer
- B) The Health and Safety Executive (HSE)
- C) The client
- D) The site manager

## 1.13

What does a risk assessment identify?

A. How to report accidents

B. The site working hours

C. The hazards and safe way of doing the job

D. Where the first-aid box is kept

## 1.14

What does the word **hazard** mean?

A. Anything at work that could harm you

B. The site accident rate

C. A type of barrier or machine guard

D. The likelihood that something might happen

## 1.15

You are about to start a job. How will you know if it needs a permit to work?

A. Other workers will tell you and you will not be allowed to start work until the permit to work has been issued

B. The Health and Safety Executive (HSE) will tell you

C. You will be told during the site induction and you will not be allowed to start work until the permit to work has been issued

D. You don't need to know, as permits to work only affect managers

## 1.16

What should you do if you cannot do a job in the way described in the method statement?

A. Make up your own way of doing the job

B. Do not start work until you have talked to your supervisor

C. Ask your workmates how they think you should do the job

D. Contact the Health and Safety Executive (HSE)

## 1.17

What does a permit to work allow?

A. The emergency services to come on to the site after an accident

B. Certain jobs to be carried out safely under more strictly controlled conditions

C. Health and Safety Executive (HSE) inspectors to visit the site

D. Untrained people to work without supervision

## 1.18

Which **three** of the following should be included in a method statement?

A. The materials, tools and equipment needed

B. The people involved and the level of competency and training required

C. The directions to the site

D. The order and correct way the work should be done

E. The risks you can take

Answers: 1.13 = C   1.14 = A   1.15 = C   1.16 = B   1.17 = B   1.18 = A, B, D

## 1.19

How would you expect to find out about site health and safety rules when you first arrive on site?

- [A] During site induction
- [B] In a letter sent to your home
- [C] By reading your employer's health and safety policy
- [D] By asking others on the site

## 1.20

Who should attend a site induction?

- [A] Just cleaners
- [B] Just architects
- [C] Just construction-related workers
- [D] Everyone going on to the site

## 1.21

Which of the following **two** topics should be covered during a site induction?

- [A] The site rules
- [B] The location of the cheapest car park
- [C] Holiday dates
- [D] The site emergency procedures
- [E] Information on local amenities

## 1.22

Why is it your employer's legal responsibility to discuss matters of health and safety with you?

- [A] So that you will never have to attend any other health and safety training
- [B] So that your employer will not have any legal responsibility for your health and safety
- [C] Because they must inform you of things that will protect your health and safety
- [D] So you do not have any responsibilities for health and safety

## 1.23

What is a toolbox talk?

- [A] A short training session on a particular safety topic
- [B] A talk that tells you where to buy tools
- [C] Your first training session when you arrive on site
- [D] A sales talk given by a tool supplier

## 1.24

What is the **main** reason for attending a site induction?

- [A] You will get to know other new starters
- [B] Risk assessments will be handed out
- [C] Site health and safety rules and site hazards will be explained
- [D] Permits to work will be handed out

A
01

General responsibilities

**1.25**

Which of the following statements **best** describes a near miss?

A) An incident where you were just too late to see what happened

B) An incident where someone could have been injured or caused damage to the environment, property or equipment

C) An incident where someone was injured and nearly had to go to hospital

D) An incident where someone was injured and nearly had to take time off work

**1.26**

How can you help to prevent accidents?

A) By reporting unsafe working conditions

B) By becoming a first aider

C) By knowing where the first-aid kit is kept

D) By knowing how to get help quickly

**1.27**

What are **two** possible consequences for employers of **not** taking measures to prevent accidents and ill health at work?

A) They could be fined or imprisoned

B) They will have to change the site layout for emergency vehicles

C) They will lose time and money due to the cost of any accident or ill health

D) They will need to employ more people

E) They will damage the environment

**1.28**

What are **two** possible consequences for you if your employer **does not** prevent accidents and ill health at work?

A) You will have to work harder

B) You may suffer an injury

C) You won't get the training you need

D) You may not be able to work, which could affect your income and family life

E) You will have worse welfare facilities

## 02 Accident reporting and recording

### 2.1

Which **two** of the following will help you find out about the site emergency procedures and emergency telephone numbers?

A Guidance from the Health and Safety Executive (HSE)

B Reading the site noticeboards

C Guidance from your local Job Centre Plus

D Attending the site induction

E Looking in the telephone directory

### 2.2

What should you do in an emergency?

A Leave site

B Phone home

C Follow the site emergency procedure

D Phone the Health and Safety Executive (HSE)

### 2.3

Where is the assembly point in an emergency?

A In the site manager's office

B At the site of the incident or accident

C In the site welfare facilities

D At the designated place

### 2.4

You have witnessed a serious accident on your site and are to be interviewed by a Health and Safety Executive (HSE) inspector. What should you do?

A Ask your supervisor what you should say to the inspector

B Not tell the inspector anything

C Co-operate and tell the inspector exactly what you saw

D Tell the inspector what your workmates have told you

### 2.5

What is the **main** objective of carrying out an accident investigation?

A To find out who is at fault

B To find out the causes in order to prevent it happening again

C To find out the cost of any damage that occurred

D To record what injuries were sustained

### 2.6

A scaffold has collapsed and you saw it happen. What should you say when you are asked about the accident?

A Nothing, as you are not a scaffold expert

B As little as possible because you don't want to get people into trouble

C Exactly what you saw

D Who you think is to blame and how they should be punished

A 02

**A**
**02**

## 2.7

When **must** you record an accident in the accident book?

- A) If you are injured in any way
- B) Only if you have to be off work
- C) Only if you have suffered a broken bone
- D) Only if you have to go to hospital

## 2.8

If someone is injured at work, who should record it in the accident book?

- A) The site manager
- B) The injured person or someone acting for them
- C) The first aider
- D) Someone from the Health and Safety Executive (HSE)

## 2.9

Which of these does **not** have to be recorded in the accident book?

- A) Your national insurance number
- B) The date and time of your accident
- C) Details of your injury
- D) Your home address

## 2.10

Which type of accidents should be recorded in the accident book?

- A) Only specified injuries, such as a broken arm or death of a person
- B) Only injuries requiring hospital treatment
- C) All accidents causing any injury
- D) Only accidents where the injured person has to stop work

## 2.11

When **must** an accident be recorded?

- A) Only when an accident causes injury to a worker as a result of working activities
- B) Only when a person is injured and will be off work for more than three days
- C) Only when an accident causes damage to plant or equipment
- D) Only when a person breaks a major bone or is concussed

## 2.12

When **must** an entry be made in the accident book?

- A) When an accident causes personal injury to any worker
- B) When the person has been off sick for three days
- C) When the accident may result in a compensation claim
- D) When management thinks it appropriate

## 2.13

Which **two** of the following items **do not** have to be recorded in an accident book?

- (A) Your national insurance number
- (B) Your telephone number
- (C) The date and time of the accident
- (D) The injuries sustained
- (E) The location of the accident

## 2.14

You suffer an injury at work and the details are recorded into the accident book. What **must** happen to this accident record?

- (A) It must be sent to the employer's insurance company at the end of the job
- (B) It must be kept in a place where anyone can read it
- (C) It must be treated as confidential under the Data Protection Act and kept for at least three years
- (D) It must be destroyed at the end of the job

## 2.15

Where should accidents that cause any injury be recorded?

- (A) In the main contractor's diary
- (B) In the accident report book
- (C) In the site engineer's day book
- (D) In the Health and Safety Executive's (HSE) accident database

## 2.16

Which of these is the **least** important reason for recording all accidents?

- (A) It might stop them happening again
- (B) Some types of accident have to be reported to the Health and Safety Executive (HSE)
- (C) Details have to be entered in the accident book
- (D) To find out who is to blame and make sure they are prosecuted

## 2.17

Why is it important to report near miss incidents on site?

- (A) Because it is the law to report all near miss incidents
- (B) To find someone to blame
- (C) It is a requirement of the CDM Regulations
- (D) To learn from them and stop them happening again

## 2.18

If you have a minor accident, who should report it?

- (A) Anyone who saw the accident happen
- (B) A sub-contractor
- (C) You
- (D) The Health and Safety Executive (HSE)

A
02

Answers: 2.13 = A, B   2.14 = C   2.15 = B   2.16 = D   2.17 = D   2.18 = C

## 2.19

If your doctor says that you contracted Weil's disease (leptospirosis) on site, why do you need to tell your employer?

A Your employer has to warn your colleagues not to go near you

B Your employer will have to report it to the Health and Safety Executive (HSE)

C Your employer will need to call pest control to remove rats on site

D The site on which you contracted it will have to be closed down

## 2.20

While working on site you get a small cut on one of your fingers. What should you do?

A Report it at the end of the day or the end of the shift

B Wash it, and if it is not a problem carrying on working

C Clean it and tell your supervisor about it later

D Report it and get first aid if necessary

## 2.21

You are injured by an accident at work. When should you report it?

A At the end of the day, before you go home

B Only if you had to take time off work

C Immediately, or as soon as possible

D The next day before you start work

## 2.22

You have been injured by an accident at work and, as a result, are absent for more than seven days. Which **two** of the following actions **must** be taken?

A The accident must be recorded in the accident book

B The emergency services must be called to find out how the accident happened

C The local hospital and the benefits office must be informed

D Your employer must inform the Health and Safety Executive (HSE)

E You must pay for any first-aid equipment used to treat your injury

## 2.23

Why should you report an accident?

A It helps the site find out who caused it

B It is a legal requirement

C So that everyone can find out what happened by reading the accident book

D So that your company will be held responsible

## 2.24

Who must you report a serious accident to?

A Site security

B The police service

C Your employer

D The ambulance service

Answers: 2.19 = B   2.20 = D   2.21 = C   2.22 = A, D   2.23 = B   2.24 = C

## 2.25

You are involved in a dangerous incident on site but no-one was injured. Who **must** you report this 'dangerous occurrence' to?

A Your site supervisor or the site manager

B The client for the project

C The rest of the workforce

D The first aider

**A**
**02**

## 2.26

What should you do if you have witnessed a serious accident on your site?

A Say nothing in case you get someone into trouble

B Ask your workmates what they think you should do

C Telephone the local hospital

D Tell your supervisor that you saw what happened

## 2.27

Your doctor tells you that you have hand-arm vibration syndrome possibly caused through work. What should you do?

A Tell no-one as it's not contagious

B Inform your site supervisor or employer

C Just inform your workmates

D Tell no-one as this is not reportable

Answers: 2.25 = A    2.26 = D    2.27 = B

## 03 Emergency procedures and first aid

### 3.1

 What does this sign mean?

A) Safety glasses cleaning station

B) Emergency eyewash station

C) Warning, risk of splashing

D) Wear eye protection

### 3.2

 What does this sign mean?

A) First aid

B) Safe to cross

C) No waiting

D) Medicine box

### 3.3

Where will you find out about emergency assembly points?

A) A risk assessment

B) A method statement

C) The site induction

D) The permit to work

### 3.4

How should you be informed about what to do in an emergency? Give **two** answers.

A) By attending the site induction

B) By looking in the health and safety file

C) By asking the Health and Safety Executive (HSE)

D) By asking at the local hospital

E) By reading the site noticeboards

### 3.5

What should **not** be in a first-aid box?

A) Bandages

B) Plasters

C) Safety pins

D) Tablets and medicines

### 3.6

If the first-aid box on site is always empty, what should you do?

A) Bring your own first-aid supplies into work

B) Find out who is taking all the first-aid supplies

C) Find out who looks after the first-aid box and let them know

D) Ignore the problem, it is always the same

## 3.7

Does your employer have to provide a first-aid box?

A Yes, every site must have one

B Only if more than 50 people work on site

C Only if more than 25 people work on site

D No, there is no legal duty to provide one

## 3.8

When would you expect eyewash bottles to be provided?

A Only on demolition sites where asbestos has to be removed

B Only on sites where refurbishment is being carried out

C On all sites where people could get something in their eyes

D On all sites where showers are needed

## 3.9

What should you do if you want to be a first aider?

A Watch a first aider treating people then try it yourself

B Ask if you can do a first-aider's course

C Buy a book on first aid and start treating people

D Speak to your doctor about it

## 3.10

What is the **first** thing you should do if you find an injured person?

A Tell your supervisor

B Check that you are not in any danger before you check the injured person

C Move the injured person to a safe place

D Ask the injured person what happened

## 3.11

If you are not trained in first aid, and someone is knocked unconscious, what should you do **first**?

A Turn them over so they are lying on their back

B Send for medical help

C Slap their face to wake them up

D Give mouth-to-mouth resuscitation

## 3.12

If someone has fallen from height and has no feeling in their legs, what should you do?

A Roll them onto their back and keep their legs straight

B Roll them onto their side and bend their legs

C Ensure they stay still and don't move them until medical help arrives

D Raise their legs to see if any feeling comes back

Answers: 3.7 = A   3.8 = C   3.9 = B   3.10 = B   3.11 = B   3.12 = C

**A**
**03**

### 3.13

If there is an emergency while you are on site, what should you do **first**?

- A  Leave the site and go home
- B  Phone home
- C  Follow the site emergency procedure
- D  Phone the Health and Safety Executive (HSE)

### 3.14

If someone working in a deep manhole has collapsed, what should you do **first**?

- A  Get someone to lower you into the manhole on a rope
- B  Climb into the manhole and give mouth-to-mouth resuscitation
- C  Go and tell your supervisor
- D  Shout and raise the alarm as a trained rescue team will be needed

### 3.15

If someone is in contact with a live cable, what should you do **first**?

- A  Phone the electricity company
- B  Dial 999 and ask for an ambulance
- C  Switch off the power and call for help
- D  Pull them away from the cable

### 3.16

If you cut your finger and it won't stop bleeding, what should you do?

- A  Wrap something around it and carry on working
- B  Tell your workmates
- C  Wash it clean then carry on working
- D  Find a first aider or get other medical help

### 3.17

If you think someone has a broken leg, what should you do?

- A  Lie them on their side in the recovery position
- B  Use your belt to strap their legs together
- C  Send for the first aider or get other help
- D  Lie them on their back

### 3.18

If someone gets grit in their eye, what is the **best** thing you can do?

- A  Hold the eye open and wipe it with clean tissue paper
- B  Ask them to rub the eye until it starts to water
- C  Tell them to blink a couple of times
- D  Hold the eye open and flush it with sterilised water or eyewash

## 3.19

Someone gets a large splinter in their hand. It is deep under the skin and it hurts. What should you do?

A Use something sharp to dig it out

B Make sure they get first aid

C Tell them to ignore it and let the splinter come out on its own

D Try to squeeze out the splinter with your thumbs

## 3.20

Someone collapses with stomach pain and there is no first aider on site. What should you do **first**?

A Get them to sit down

B Get someone to call the emergency services

C Get them to lie down in the recovery position

D Give them some painkillers

## 3.21

Someone has got a nail in their foot. You are not a first aider. Why **must** you **not** pull the nail out?

A You will let air and bacteria get into the wound

B The nail is helping to reduce the bleeding

C It will prove that the casualty was not wearing safety boots

D The nail is helping to keep their boot on

## 3.22

If someone burns their hand, what is the **best** thing you can do?

A Put the hand into cold water or under a cold running tap

B Tell them to carry on working to exercise the hand

C Rub barrier cream or Vaseline® into the burn

D Wrap your handkerchief around the burn

## 3.23

What is the one thing a first aider **cannot** do for you?

A Give mouth-to-mouth resuscitation

B Stop any bleeding

C Give you medicines without authorisation

D Treat you if you are unconscious

**A**
**03**

Answers: 3.19 = B   3.20 = B   3.21 = B   3.22 = A   3.23 = C

# B

# Health and welfare

## Contents

## 04  Health and welfare

### 4.1

What sort of rest area should your employer provide on site?

A  A covered area

B  A covered area and some chairs

C  A covered area, tables and chairs, and something to heat water and food

D  Nothing, employers don't have to provide rest areas

### 4.2

What are the legal minimum facilities that should be provided on site for washing your hands?

A  Nothing, there is no need to provide washing facilities

B  A bowl, kettle and towel

C  A cold water standpipe and paper towels

D  Hot and cold water, soap and a way to dry your hands

### 4.3

The toilets on your site are always dirty or do not flush. What should you do?

A  Try not to use the toilets while you are at work

B  Tell the person in charge of the site about the problem

C  Try to fix the fault yourself

D  See if you can use the toilets in a nearby café or pub

### 4.4

It is your first day on site. You find that there is nowhere to wash your hands. What should you do?

A  Wait until you get home, then wash them

B  Go to a local café or pub and use the washbasin in their toilet

C  Speak to your supervisor or the site manager about the problem

D  There is nothing you can do as the site does not have to provide washing facilities

### 4.5

What should you use to clean very dirty hands?

A  Soap and water

B  Thinners

C  White spirit

D  Paraffin

### 4.6

Why should you **not** use white spirit or other solvents to clean your hands?

A  They could strip the protective oils from the skin

B  They may remove the top layer of skin

C  They could block the pores of the skin

D  They may carry harmful bacteria that attack the skin

## 4.7

What are **two** ways of reducing the risk of transferring hazardous substances from your hands to your mouth?

- [A] Wearing protective gloves while you are working
- [B] Washing your hands before eating
- [C] Putting barrier cream on your hands before eating
- [D] Wearing protective gloves then turning them inside out before eating
- [E] Washing your work gloves then putting them on again before eating

## 4.8

You can catch an infection called tetanus from contaminated land or water. How does it get into your body?

- [A] Through your nose when you breathe
- [B] Through an open cut in your skin
- [C] Through your mouth when you eat or drink
- [D] It doesn't, it only infects animals and not people

## 4.9

What condition can be caused by direct sunlight on bare skin?

- [A] Dermatitis
- [B] Rickets
- [C] Acne
- [D] Skin cancer

## 4.10

What is the main issue with using barrier cream to protect your skin?

- [A] It costs too much to use every day
- [B] Many harmful substances go straight through it
- [C] It is difficult to wash off
- [D] It can irritate your skin

**B**
04

## 4.11

When should you apply skin barrier cream?

- [A] Before you start work
- [B] When you finish work
- [C] As part of first-aid treatment
- [D] When you can't find your gloves

## 4.12

What can be caused by exposure to engine oil and other mineral oils?

- [A] Skin problems
- [B] Heart disease
- [C] Breathing problems
- [D] Vibration white finger

## 4.13

What can cause occupational dermatitis?

- [A] Hand-arm vibration
- [B] Contact with another person with dermatitis
- [C] Contact with some types of strong chemicals or substances
- [D] Sunlight

Answers: 4.7 = A, B   4.8 = B   4.9 = D   4.10 = B   4.11 = A   4.12 = A   4.13 = C

## 4.14

Which of the following species of animal is the most likely carrier of Weil's disease (leptospirosis) on construction sites?

A Rabbits

B Rats

C Squirrels

D Mice

## 4.15

How can everyone on site help keep rats away?

A Put rat traps around the site

B Ask the local authority to put down rat poison

C Throw food scraps over the fence or hoarding

D Only put food and drink rubbish in bins provided

## 4.16

In what situation are you **most** likely to catch Weil's disease (leptospirosis)?

A If you work near wet ground, waterways or sewers

B If you work near air-conditioning units

C If you work fixing showers or baths

D If you drink water from a standpipe

## 4.17

What other illness can be easily confused with the early signs of Weil's disease (leptospirosis)?

A Dermatitis

B Diabetes

C Hay fever

D Influenza (flu)

## 4.18

Your doctor has given you some medication. Which of these questions is the most important?

A Will it make me unsafe to work or operate machinery?

B Will I work more slowly?

C Will my supervisor find out?

D Will I fail a drugs test?

## 4.19

You suspect someone has been drinking alcohol or is still over the alcohol limit. What should you do?

A Get them to drink plenty of strong coffee before they go back to work

B Tell them your concerns and see that they are safely removed from site

C Ask them to stay away for an hour and then go back to work

D Get them to eat and drink something, wait 30 minutes and then go back to work

Answers: 4.14 = B   4.15 = D   4.16 = A   4.17 = D   4.18 = A   4.19 = B

# 05 Personal protective equipment

## 5.1

When do you need to wear eye protection?

- A) On very bright, sunny days
- B) If there is a risk of eye injury and if it is the site rules
- C) When your employer can afford it
- D) Only if you work with chemicals

## 5.2

What should you wear if there is a risk of materials flying into your eyes?

- A) Tinted welding goggles
- B) Laser safety glasses
- C) Chemical-resistant goggles
- D) Impact-resistant goggles

## 5.3

What type of eye protection do you need to wear if you are using a cartridge-operated tool or compressed gas tool (nail gun)?

- A) Light eye protection or safety glasses
- B) Normal prescription glasses or sunglasses
- C) Impact-rated goggles
- D) None – they aren't needed as there is a minimal risk of injury

## 5.4

You need to use a grinder, cut-off saw, cartridge tool or nail gun. What type of eye protection will you need?

- A) Impact-resistant goggles or full face shield
- B) Welding goggles
- C) Reading glasses or sunglasses
- D) Light eye protection (safety glasses)

## 5.5

What will safety footwear with a protective mid-sole protect you from?

- A) Twisting your ankle
- B) Spillages which may burn the sole of your foot
- C) Nails or sharp objects puncturing the sole of your foot if you stand on them
- D) Getting blisters in warm, wet conditions

## 5.6

When should you wear safety footwear on site?

- A) Only when working at ground level or outside
- B) Until the site starts to look finished
- C) All the time
- D) When you are working all day on site and not just visiting

**B**
**05**

### 5.7

What condition could be prevented if you wear the correct gloves while handling a hazardous substance?

A Skin disease

B Vibration white finger

C Raynaud's syndrome

D Arthritis

### 5.8

Do all types of glove protect hands against chemicals?

A Yes, all gloves are made to the same standard

B Only if you put barrier cream on your hands as well

C No, different types of glove protect against different types of hazard

D Only if you cover the gloves with barrier cream

### 5.9

Which of the following statements about using power tools while wearing gloves is **false**?

A Anti-vibration gloves will protect you against the effects of vibration

B Gloves will keep your hands warm and dry, which reduces the effects of vibration

C Gloves provide a better grip so you don't need to grip too tightly, which reduces the effects of vibration

D Gloves will protect you from cuts and abrasions

### 5.10

You need to wear a full body harness. You have never used one before. What should you do?

A Ask for expert advice and training

B Ask someone already wearing a harness to show you what to do

C Try to work it out for yourself

D Read the instruction book

### 5.11

When is the only time that you do **not** need to wear head protection on site?

A If you are self-employed

B If you are working alone

C If you are in a safe area, like the site office or canteen

D If you are working in very hot weather

### 5.12

How should you wear your safety helmet to get maximum protection from it?

A  Back to front

B  Pushed back on your head

C  Square on your head

D  Pulled forward

## 5.13

What should you do If you drop your safety helmet from height onto a hard surface?

A Repair any cracks then carry on wearing it

B Make sure there are no cracks then carry on wearing it

C Work without a safety helmet until you can get a new one

D Stop work and get a new safety helmet

## 5.14

Which of the following statements about wearing a safety helmet in hot weather is **true**?

A You can drill holes in it to keep your head cool

B You can wear it back-to-front if it is more comfortable that way

C You must take it off during the hottest part of the day

D You must wear it at all times and in the right way

## 5.15

When working in cold weather, what additional measures can you wear under your hard hat?

A A baseball cap, with a peak to keep the rain out of your eyes

B A jumper with a detachable hood

C A woolly hat

D Manufacturer's attachment addition for use in cold weather

## 5.16

You have been given disposable earplugs to use, but they keep falling out. What should you do?

A Throw them away and work without them

B Stop work until you get more suitable ones and are shown how to fit them

C Put two earplugs in each ear so they stay in place

D Put rolled-up tissue paper in each ear

**B**
**05**

## 5.17

What should you do if you have to shout to make yourself heard on site?

A Raise your voice and carry on working

B Stop work and raise it with your supervisor

C Pack up and go home

D Tell the person making the noise to stop work

## 5.18

When **must** your employer provide you with personal protective equipment (PPE)?

A Twice a year

B If you pay for it

C If it is in the contract

D If you need to be protected

Answers: 5.13 = D    5.14 = D    5.15 = D    5.16 = B    5.17 = B    5.18 = D

## 5.19

Do you have to pay for any personal protective equipment (PPE) you need?

A Yes, you must pay for all of it

B Only if you need to replace lost or damaged PPE

C Yes, but you only have to pay half the cost

D No, your employer must pay for it

## 5.20

Who should provide you with any personal protective equipment (PPE) you need, including the means to maintain it?

A Your employer

B You must buy your own

C Anyone on site with a budget

D No-one has a duty to provide it

## 5.21

What should you do if your personal protective equipment (PPE) gets damaged?

A Throw it away and work without it

B Stop what you are doing until it is replaced

C Carry on wearing it but work more quickly

D Try to repair it

## 5.22

If you have to work outdoors in bad weather, why should your employer supply you with correctly fitting waterproof clothing?

A So you need to take fewer breaks

B You need protecting from the weather and are less likely to get muscle strains if you are warm and dry

C You are less likely to catch Weil's disease (leptospirosis) if you are warm and dry

D They prevent slips and trips

## 5.23

Which of these statements about personal protective equipment (PPE) is **not** true?

A You must pay for any damage or loss

B You must store it correctly when you are not using it

C You must report any damage or loss to your supervisor

D You must use it as instructed

## 5.24

You are about to start a job. How will you know if you need any extra personal protective equipment (PPE)?

A By looking at your employer's health and safety policy

B You will always need it

C From the risk assessment or method statement

D A letter will be sent to your home

## 5.25

When should high visibility clothing be replaced?

[A] If it is soiled or damaged

[B] When it is one year old

[C] When it has been washed

[D] If it has been left outside in adverse weather conditions

B
05

## 06 Dust and fumes (respiratory risks)

**B**
**06**

### 6.1

What is the biggest cause of **long-term** health issues in the construction industry?

A Loud noise

B Being struck by a vehicle

C Slipping and tripping

D Breathing in hazardous dust and fumes

### 6.2

If you use a power tool to cut or grind materials, why must the dust be collected and not allowed to get into the air?

A To save time and avoid having to clear up the mess

B Most dust can be harmful if breathed in

C The tool will go faster if the dust is collected

D You do not need a machine guard if the dust is collected

### 6.3

You have been asked to do some work that will create dust. What should you do?

A You should not do the work. Dust is highly dangerous

B Use equipment to eliminate or reduce the dust, and wear the correct personal protective equipment (PPE)

C Start work – no controls are needed as dust cannot cause serious harm or injury

D Work for short periods at a time

### 6.4

You are planning work that needs to use a power tool to cut or grind materials. Give **two** ways to control the dust?

A Work slowly and carefully

B Fit a dust extractor or collector to the machine

C Wet cutting

D Keep the area clean and tidy

E Wear a dust mask or respirator

### 6.5

Where are you likely to breathe in the highest quantities of dust when drilling, cutting, sanding or grinding?

A Outside on a still day

B Outside on a windy day

C In a small room

D In a large indoor space

Answers: 6.1 = D    6.2 = B    6.3 = B    6.4 = B, C    6.5 = C

## 6.6

What should you **not** do when sweeping up after drilling, cutting, sanding or grinding?

A) Dampen down the area

B) Make sure there is plenty of ventilation

C) Put your protective mask back on

D) Work as quickly as possible to minimise exposure to dust

## 6.7

What is the **best** way to limit exposure to dust when using a power tool?

A) Stop dust getting into the air

B) Stand downwind of any dust

C) Do the work quickly

D) Only undertake the work during damp or wet weather

## 6.8

What is it **not** important to check when assessing the use of on-tool extraction to control dust from a power tool?

A) That the extraction unit and filter rating is the correct type

B) That the extraction filters are clear and the unit is extracting dust

C) That the operative knows how to use the power tool correctly

D) That the extraction unit has not been used before

## 6.9

What **must** you ensure when using water to keep dust down when cutting?

A) That there is as much water as possible

B) That the water flow is correctly adjusted

C) That somebody stands next to you to pour water from a bottle

D) That water is poured onto the surface before you start cutting

**B**
06

## 6.10

What should you do if the water you are using to control dust runs out?

A) Put on additional respiratory protection

B) Stop and refill the water

C) Ask everyone to clear the area and then carry on

D) Carry on but get someone to sweep up afterwards

Answers: 6.6 = D   6.7 = A   6.8 = D   6.9 = B   6.10 = B

**B**
06

## 6.11

When drilling, cutting, sanding or grinding what is the **best** way to protect your long-term health from harmful dust?

A  Use dust extraction or wet cut and wear a hard hat, hi-vis jacket and light eye protection

B  Wear a FFP3-rated dust mask and impact goggles

C  Wear any disposable dust mask, hearing protection and impact goggles

D  Use dust extraction or wet cut, wear a FFP3-rated dust mask, hearing protection and impact goggles

## 6.12

You have been given a dust mask to protect you against hazardous fumes. What should you do?

A  Do not start work until you have the correct respiratory protective equipment (RPE)

B  Do the job wearing the mask but work quickly

C  Start work but take regular breaks

D  Wear a second dust mask on top of the first one

## 6.13

Which of the following do you **not** need to do to ensure that someone's mask works?

A  Check the mask is the correct type needed

B  Check the wearer has passed a face-fit test wearing the mask

C  Check it is being worn correctly

D  Immerse it in water to ensure the seals are tight

## 6.14

In general, how long can you use the same disposable mask for?

A  Five working days

B  Until it is too dirty to wear

C  One day or one shift

D  28 days

## 6.15

You need special respiratory protective equipment (RPE) to handle a chemical. None has been provided. What should you do?

A  Get on with the job but try to work quickly

B  Do not start work until you have been given the correct RPE and training

C  Start the work but take regular breaks

D  Sniff the substance to see if it makes you feel ill

## 6.16

Which of these activities does **not** create harmful silica dust?

A) Sawing timber and plywood

B) Cutting kerbs, stone, paving slabs, bricks and blocks

C) Breaking up concrete floors and screeds

D) Chasing out walls and mortar joints or sweeping up rubble

## 6.17

What can cause occupational asthma?

A) Exposure to loud noise

B) Exposure to rat urine

C) Skin contact with any hazardous substance

D) Breathing in hazardous dust, fumes or vapours

## 6.18

What illness might you develop if you breathe in dust and fumes over time?

A) Occupational lung disease

B) Occupational dermatitis

C) Skin cancer

D) Laryngitis

## 6.19

Exposure to which of the following may **not** result in lung disease?

A) Asbestos

B) Bird droppings

C) Strong smells

D) Silica dust

## 6.20

What should you do if you find pigeon droppings and nests in an area where you are required to work?

A) Carry on with your work carefully, so you don't disturb them

B) Stop work and seek advice

C) Try to catch the pigeons

D) Wait for the pigeons to fly away before carrying on with your work

## 6.21

Which of the following is **not** a health effect of being exposed to paints and resins which have high levels of solvents?

A) Headaches and sickness

B) Drowsiness or poor coordination

C) Dermatitis or skin problems

D) Hearing loss

**B**
06

Answers: 6.16 = A   6.17 = D   6.18 = A   6.19 = C   6.20 = B   6.21 = D

## 07 Noise and vibration

### 7.1

Noise can damage your hearing. What is an early sign of this?

- [A] There are no early signs
- [B] Temporary deafness or a ringing noise in your ears
- [C] A skin rash around your ears
- [D] Regular ear infections

### 7.2

How can noise affect your health? Give **two** answers.

- [A] Temporary hearing loss
- [B] Ear infections
- [C] Permanent hearing loss
- [D] Waxy ears
- [E] Dizziness and nausea

### 7.3

If you have a ringing sound in your ears after working with noisy equipment, what does this mean?

- [A] Your hearing has been temporarily damaged
- [B] You have also been subjected to vibration
- [C] Your hearing protection was working properly
- [D] The noise level was high but acceptable

### 7.4

Can the damage by exposure to noise over a long period of time be reversed?

- [A] Yes, with time
- [B] Yes, if you have an operation
- [C] No, the damage is permanent
- [D] Yes, if you change jobs

### 7.5

What should you do if you think the noise at work may have damaged your hearing?

- [A] Plug your ears with cotton wool to stop any more damage
- [B] Nothing, as the damage has already been done
- [C] Go off sick
- [D] Ask your employer or doctor to arrange a hearing test

### 7.6

What does wearing hearing protection do?

- [A] Stops you hearing all noise
- [B] Reduces damaging noise to an acceptable level
- [C] Repairs your hearing if it is damaged
- [D] Makes you hear better

**B**
07

Answers: 7.1 = B   7.2 = A, C   7.3 = A   7.4 = C   7.5 = D   7.6 = B

## 7.7

What are **two** recommended ways to protect your hearing?

A Rolled tissue paper

B Cotton wool pads over your ears

C Earplugs

D Soft cloth pads over your ears

E Ear defenders

## 7.8

If you need to wear disposable earplugs how should you insert them so they protect your hearing from damage?

A Soak them in water, squeeze them out and then insert them into your ear canal

B Do not roll or fold them, and insert them half way into your ear canal

C Roll them up and insert them as far as you can, while pulling the top of your ear up to open up the ear canal

D Fold them in half, pull on your earlobe and wedge them into your ear canal

## 7.9

Someone near you is using noisy equipment and you have no hearing protection. What should you do?

A Ask them to stop what they are doing

B Carry on with your work, you are not the person using the equipment

C Leave the area until you have the correct personal protective equipment (PPE)

D Speak to the other person's supervisor

B
07

## 7.10

Noise levels may be a problem if, in general, you have to shout to be heard when someone is standing how far away?

A 2 m away

B 4 m away

C 5 m away

D 6 m away

## 7.11

What should you do if you need to wear ear defenders but an ear pad is missing from one of the shells?

A Leave them off and work without any hearing protection

B Put them on and go on to site with them as they are

C Do not visit noisy areas until they are replaced

D Take an ear pad from another set of ear defenders

Answers: 7.7 = C, E   7.8 = C   7.9 = C   7.10 = A   7.11 = C

**B**
**07**

## 7.12

What **must** you do when working in a hearing protection zone?

A) Not make any noise

B) Wear the correct hearing protection at all times

C) Take hearing protection with you in case you need to use it

D) Wear hearing protection if the noise gets too loud for you

## 7.13

Why is over exposure to vibratory tools and equipment a serious issue?

A) There are no early warning signs of damage caused by vibration

B) The long-term effects of vibration are not known

C) There is no way that exposure to vibration can be prevented

D) Vibration can cause a disabling injury that cannot be cured

## 7.14

What is hand-arm vibration syndrome (HAVS), which is also known as vibration white finger?

A) A mild skin rash that will go away

B) A serious skin condition that will not clear up

C) Severe frostbite

D) A condition that can lead to permanent damage

## 7.15

What health problem can be caused by hand-arm vibration syndrome (HAVS)?

A) Skin cancer

B) Skin irritation, like dermatitis

C) Blisters on your hands and arms

D) Damaged blood vessels and nerves in your fingers and hands

## 7.16

What are **three** early signs of vibration white finger or hand-arm vibration syndrome (HAVS)?

A) Temporary loss of feeling in the fingers

B) Fingertips turn white

C) Rash on the fingers

D) Tingling or pins and needles sensation in the fingers

E) Blisters

## 7.17

You are **less** likely to suffer from hand-arm vibration syndrome (HAVS) if you feel which of the following?

A) Cold but dry

B) Cold and wet

C) Warm and dry

D) Wet but warm

Answers: 7.12 = B   7.13 = D   7.14 = D   7.15 = D   7.16 = A, B, D   7.17 = C

**7.18**

Which of these tools is **most** likely to cause vibration white finger?

- A Handsaw
- B Hammer drill
- C Hammer and chisel
- D Battery-powered screwdriver

**7.19**

You have been using a vibrating tool. The ends of your fingers are starting to tingle. What does this mean?

- A You can carry on using the tool but you must loosen your grip
- B You must not use this tool, or any other vibrating tool, ever again
- C You need to report your symptoms before they cause a problem
- D You can carry on using the tool but you must hold it tighter

**7.20**

If you have to use a vibrating tool, what would you expect your supervisor to do?

- A Measure the level of vibration while you use the tool
- B Explain the risk assessment, the safest way and length of time each day that you can use the tool
- C Watch you use the tool to assess the level of vibration
- D Help you to make up your own safe system of work

**7.21**

If you need to use a vibrating tool, even for a short time, how can you help reduce the risk of hand-arm vibration?

- A Do not grip the tool too tightly
- B Hold the tool away from you, at arm's length
- C Use more force
- D Hold the tool more tightly

**B**
07

**7.22**

If you have to use a vibrating tool, how can you help reduce the effects of hand-arm vibration?

- A Hold the tool tightly
- B Do the work in short spells
- C Do the job in one long burst
- D Only use one hand on the tool at a time

Answers: 7.18 = B   7.19 = C   7.20 = B   7.21 = A   7.22 = B

## 08  Hazardous substances

### 8.1

Where might you come across asbestos?

- [A] In a house built between 1950 and 1990
- [B] In any building built or refurbished before the year 2000
- [C] In industrial buildings built between 1920 and 1990
- [D] Asbestos has now been removed from all buildings

### 8.2

After asbestos, which of the following causes the **most** ill health to construction workers?

- [A] Wood and MDF dust
- [B] Diesel fumes
- [C] Silica dust
- [D] Resin, solvent and paint vapours

### 8.3

What illness might you develop if you breathe in asbestos dust?

- [A] Aching muscles and painful joints
- [B] Throat infections
- [C] Lung diseases
- [D] Dizziness and headaches

### 8.4

Exposure to asbestos fibres may result in which disease?

- [A] Mesothelioma
- [B] Asbestosis
- [C] Lung cancer
- [D] All of these answers

### 8.5

How can asbestos be correctly identified?

- [A] The dust gives off a strong smell
- [B] By getting a sample analysed in a laboratory
- [C] By the colour of the dust
- [D] By putting a piece in water and seeing if it dissolves

### 8.6

What training do you need to work with or remove asbestos cement products?

- [A] General asbestos awareness training
- [B] Gaining a CSCS card
- [C] Training for non-licensable asbestos work
- [D] None – anyone can work with asbestos cement

**B**
**08**

Answers: 8.1 = B   8.2 = C   8.3 = C   8.4 = D   8.5 = B   8.6 = C

## 8.7

If you think you have found some asbestos, what is the **first** thing you should do?

A) Stop work and warn others

B) Take a sample to your supervisor

C) Put the bits in a bin and carry on with your work

D) Find the first aider

## 8.8

What PPE or RPE is necessary if you are doing non-licensed work on asbestos-containing materials?

A) Disposable overalls (type 5)

B) Suitable respiratory protective equipment (RPE) (e.g. disposable face mask with a FFP3 rating)

C) Laceless footwear

D) All of these answers

## 8.9

Which of the following is notifiable non-licensed asbestos work?

A) Encapsulating and sealing in asbestos-containing material

B) Cleaning up small quantities of asbestos-containing dust that does not exceed the control limit

C) Drilling into textured coating to install fixtures and fittings

D) Removing asbestos sheet products where the material will be broken or damaged

## 8.10

 Which **three** of the following should be labelled with this sign?

A) Asbestos waste

B) Raw asbestos

C) Any product containing asbestos

D) Plasterboard waste

E) Recyclable waste

**B**
08

## 8.11

Why are wet cement, mortar and concrete hazardous to your health?

A) They can cause dizziness and headaches

B) They can cause skin burns and dermatitis

C) They can cause muscle aches

D) They can cause arc eye

## 8.12

Why should you wear wellington boots when working in wet cement?

A) To stop your trousers getting wet

B) To keep your feet warm

C) To prevent dermatitis and skin burns

D) To allow you to walk faster through the cement

## 8.13

Cement bags have an additive to help prevent allergic dermatitis. When using a new bag what should be checked to help protect you from developing allergic dermatitis?

A That the bag is undamaged

B That the use by date has not expired

C That it has been stored in a dry place

D That the contents are not hard and gone off

## 8.14

Which of the following provides health and safety information about a hazardous substance?

A The site diary

B The delivery note

C The COSHH assessment

D The manual handling assessment

## 8.15

What does a COSHH assessment tell you?

A How to lift heavy loads and how to protect yourself

B How to work safely in confined spaces

C How a substance might harm you and how to protect yourself when you are using it

D How noise levels are assessed and how to protect your hearing

## 8.16

What is the safest way to use a hazardous substance?

A Getting on with the job as quickly as possible

B Reading your employer's health and safety policy

C Understanding the COSHH assessment and following the instructions

D Asking someone who has already used it

## 8.17

You need to use a hazardous substance. Who should explain the health risks and safe method of work you need to follow (the COSHH assessment) before you start?

A A Health and Safety Executive (HSE) inspector

B The site first aider

C Your supervisor or employer

D The site security people

## 8.18

You find an unmarked container that you think might contain chemicals. What is the first thing you should do?

A Smell the chemical to see what it is

B Put it in a bin to get rid of it

C Ensure it remains undisturbed and report it

D Taste the chemical to see what it is

Answers: 8.13 = B   8.14 = C   8.15 = C   8.16 = C   8.17 = C   8.18 = C

**B**
08

## 8.19

If you see either of these labels on a substance what should you do?

- A) Do not use it as the substance is poisonous
- B) Find out what protection you need as the substance is corrosive and can damage your skin upon contact
- C) Wash your hands after you have used the substance
- D) Find out what hand cleaner you will need as the substance will not wash off easily

## 8.20

If you see either of these labels on a substance what should you do?

- A) Find out what protection you need as the substance is harmful and could damage your health
- B) Use it sparingly as the substance is expensive
- C) Wear gloves as the substance can burn your skin
- D) Do not use it as the substance is poisonous

## 8.21

How can you tell if a product is hazardous?

- A) By warning symbols on the container or packaging label
- B) By the shape of the container
- C) It will always be in a black container
- D) It will always be in a cardboard box

**B
08**

## 8.22

What does the word **sensitiser** mean on the packaging of a substance?

- A) That you could become allergic to it and have allergic reactions
- B) It must be mixed with water before you can use it
- C) It is perfectly safe to use without personal protective equipment (PPE)
- D) It should not be used under any circumstances

## 8.23

If you see either of these labels on a substance what should you do?

- A) Make sure it is stored out of the reach of children
- B) Use the substance very carefully and make sure you don't spill it or splash it on yourself
- C) Do not use the substance as it is poisonous
- D) Find out what protection you need as the substance is toxic, even in low quantities

Hazardous substances

## 8.24

If you see either of these labels on a substance what should you do?

A Find out how to handle the substance as it is fragile

B Find out how to use the substance safely as it could explode

C Find out how to use the substance safely as it could catch fire easily

D Do not use the substance as it could kill you

## 8.25

If you see either of these labels on a substance what should you do?

A Dispose of the substance or contents by burning

B Find out how to use the substance safely as it could explode

C Find out how to use the substance safely as it is flammable (could catch fire easily)

D Warm up the contents first, with heat or a naked flame

## 8.26

 What does this sign mean?

A Substance can explode

B Substance will cause heartburn if swallowed

C Substance can glow in the dark

D Substance can cause serious long-term health hazards

**B**
08

# 09 Manual handling

## 9.1

Which of the following is a manual handling task?

A Lifting materials with a crane

B Climbing ladders or stairs

C Activities involving pushing, pulling, lowering and lifting

D Getting in and out of a vehicle used at work

## 9.2

You are using a wheelbarrow to move a heavy load. Is this manual handling?

A No, because the wheelbarrow is carrying the load

B Only if the load slips off the wheelbarrow

C Yes, you are still manually handling the load

D Only if the wheelbarrow is pulled instead of pushed

## 9.3

What is the **main** reason for ensuring safe manual handling techniques in the workplace?

A To complete the job quickly

B To prevent personal injury

C To satisfy the client's requirements

D To be prepared for safety inspections

## 9.4

What is an advantage of adopting safe manual handling methods?

A You can protect your back and reduce the risk of injury

B You can increase your strength

C You can leave work earlier that day

D You can lift heavier loads

## 9.5

Which part of your body is most likely to be injured if you lift heavy loads?

A Your knees

B Your back

C Your shoulders

D Your elbows

## 9.6

What **must** all workers do under the regulations for manual handling?

A Wear back support belts when lifting anything

B Make a list of all the heavy things they have to carry

C Lift any size of load once the risk assessment has been done

D Follow their employer's safe systems of work

B
09

**B**
**09**

### 9.7

Who should be involved in creating the safe system of work for your manual handling?

A You

B Your supervisor or employer

C You, and your supervisor or employer

D The Health and Safety Executive (HSE)

### 9.8

You have to lift a heavy load. What **must** your employer do?

A Make sure your supervisor is there to advise while you lift

B Do a risk assessment of the task

C Nothing, it is part of your job to lift loads

D Watch you while you lift the load

### 9.9

What **three** of the following factors must you think about to lift a load safely?

A Its size and shape

B Its weight

C How to grip or hold it firmly

D Is the content of the load insured

E What is the value of the load

### 9.10

A heavy load has been delivered to site. What is the **first** thing that should be considered before trying to move it?

A How far the load would have to be carried manually

B How the risk of manual handling could be reduced

C How many people are needed to lift the load

D How the need to manually lift the load could be avoided

### 9.11

You need to move a load that might be too heavy for you. What **three** methods could you use?

A Dividing the load into smaller loads if possible

B Getting someone to help you

C Using an aid, such as a trolley or wheelbarrow

D Testing the load's weight by picking it up for a short time

E Dragging the load to avoid lifting it

## 9.12

You have to move a load that might be too heavy for you. You cannot divide it into smaller parts and there is no-one to help you. What should you do?

A  Do not move the load until you have found a safe method

B  Get a forklift truck, even though you have not been trained to use it

C  Try to lift it using the correct lifting methods

D  Lift and move the load quickly to avoid injury

## 9.13

What are **two** risks of carrying a load in cold, damp conditions?

A  Your ability to carry the load will be reduced

B  The path could be slippery

C  You will need to work more quickly to warm up

D  The load will be easier to carry

E  The load will feel lighter due to the cold conditions

## 9.14

You are using a trolley to move a heavy load a long distance but a wheel comes off. What should you do?

A  Carry the load the rest of the way

B  Ask someone to help you pull the trolley the rest of the way

C  Drag the trolley on your own the rest of the way

D  Find another way to move the load

**B**
09

## 9.15

You need to lift a load that is not heavy, but it is so big that you cannot see in front of you. What should you do?

A  Ask someone to help carry the load so that you can both see ahead

B  Get someone to walk next to you and give directions

C  Get someone to walk in front of you and tell others to get out of the way

D  Move the load on your own because it is so large that anyone in your way is sure to see it

## 9.16

What should you do if you have to carry a load down a steep slope?

A  Walk backwards down the slope to help you balance

B  Carry the load on your shoulder

C  Assess whether you can still carry the load safely

D  Put the load down and let gravity move it down the slope

Answers: 9.12 = A   9.13 = A, B   9.14 = D   9.15 = A   9.16 = C

**B 09**

### 9.17

You have been told how to lift a heavy load, but you think there is a better way to do it. What should you do?

A Ignore what you have been told and do it your way

B Ask your workmates to decide which way you should do it

C Discuss your idea with your supervisor

D Forget your idea and do it the way you have been told

### 9.18

Your new job involves some manual handling. An old injury means that you have a weak back. What should you do?

A Tell your supervisor you can lift anything

B Tell your supervisor that lifting might be a problem

C Try some lifting then tell your supervisor about your back

D Tell your supervisor about your back if it gets injured again

### 9.19

What is the outcome of wearing a back support belt when lifting?

A You can lift any load without being injured

B You can safely lift more than usual

C You could face the same risk of injury as when you are not wearing one

D It will crush your backbone and damage it

### 9.20

How should you stand if you need to lift a load from the floor?

A With your feet together, legs straight and back bent

B With your feet together and knees bent, in a deep squatting position

C With your feet slightly apart, one leg slightly forward, and knees bent

D With your feet wide apart, legs straight, and back bent

### 9.21

What does it mean if you to have to twist or turn your body when you lift and place a load?

A That the weight you can lift safely is less than usual

B The weight you can lift safely is more than usual

C Nothing, you can lift the same weight as usual

D You must wear a back brace

### 9.22

You need to reach above your head and lower a load to the floor. Which of these is **not** true?

A It will be more difficult to keep your back straight and chin tucked in

B You will put extra stress on your arms and your back

C You can safely handle more weight than usual

D The load will be more difficult to control

## 9.23

You have to move a load while you are sitting down. How much can you lift safely?

A. Less than the usual amount

B. The usual amount

C. Twice the usual amount

D. Three times the usual amount

## 9.24

You need to move a load that is heavier on one side than the other. How should you pick it up?

A. With the heavy side towards you

B. With the heavy side away from you

C. With the heavy side on your strong arm

D. With the heavy side on your weak arm

## 9.25

You have to get something from the back of a van but it's too far inside to handle. What should you do?

A. Clear a path inside the van so you can get a good grip on it

B. Drag it closer, then lift it

C. Lean over slightly while moving it closer

D. Leave it in the back of the van

## 9.26

Your job requires you to move the same sized load several times a minute from one place to another. Could this be a problem?

A. Not if the load is below the recommended weight for lifting

B. Yes, as repetition introduces additional strain to the body

C. No, it won't need a risk assessment if the load is light

D. Only if, as work progresses, the load cannot be moved as often as required

**B**
09

## 9.27

Which of the following is the **best** method to help minimise the risk of injury when manual handling?

A. Safely using lifting aids

B. Making the area of site flatter before performing the task

C. Asking a trained person to carry the load

D. Not having any heavy objects on site

Answers: 9.23 = A   9.24 = A   9.25 = A   9.26 = B   9.27 = A

**B
09**

## 9.28

What is the **main** reason for using lifting aids when undertaking a manual handling activity?

- (A) They help reduce the risk of personal injury
- (B) You do not require training to use them
- (C) You can lift any load with a lifting aid
- (D) Lifting aids are expensive so should be used

## 9.29

What **two** things are important for the use of manual handling lifting aids?

- (A) The user must hold a CSCS card
- (B) The lifting aid can only be used outside
- (C) The lifting aid must be designed for the task
- (D) The lifting aid must not be more than six months old
- (E) The user must be trained in the correct use of the lifting aid

# C

# General safety

**Contents**

# 10 Safety signs

## 10.1

 What are blue and white signs?

- A. Mandatory signs – meaning you must do something
- B. Prohibition signs – meaning you must not do something
- C. Warning signs – alerting you to hazards or danger
- D. Safe condition signs – giving you information

## 10.2

 What does this sign mean?

- A. Wear hearing protection if you want to
- B. You must wear hearing protection
- C. No personal stereos or MP3 players
- D. Caution, noisy machinery

## 10.3

 What does this sign mean?

- A. Safety glasses cleaning station
- B. Warning – bright lights or lasers
- C. Caution – poor lighting
- D. You must wear safety eye protection

## 10.4

 What does this sign mean?

- A. Safety boots or safety shoes must be worn
- B. Wellington boots must be worn
- C. Be aware of slip and trip hazards
- D. No dirty footwear past this point

## 10.5

 What does this sign mean?

- A. You must carry safety gloves at all times
- B. Dispose of used safety gloves here
- C. Safety gloves do not need to be worn
- D. Safety gloves must be worn

## 10.6

 What does this sign mean?

- A. Wear white clothes at night
- B. Hi-vis clothing must be worn
- C. Managers should wear a jacket
- D. Cover up bare arms

## 10.7

 What does this sign mean?

A. Only white safety helmets allowed in this area

B. Remove safety helmets in this area

C. Safety helmets must be worn

D. Dispose of damaged safety helmets here

## 10.8

 What does this sign mean?

A. Safety overalls must be worn

B. Only white overalls allowed in this area

C. Remove overalls in this area

D. Long-sleeved tops must be worn

## 10.9

 What are round red and white signs with a diagonal line?

A. Mandatory signs – meaning you must do something

B. Prohibition signs – meaning you must not do something

C. Warning signs – alerting you to hazards or danger

D. Safe condition signs – giving you information

## 10.10

 What does this sign mean?

A. Smoking is allowed

B. Danger flammable materials present

C. No smoking

D. No explosives or naked flames

## 10.11

 What does this sign mean?

A. No lone working

B. No entry without a hard hat

C. No pedestrians, or entry for people on foot

D. No entry during the day

C
10

## 10.12

 What does this sign mean?

A. Do not jump across any gaps in the scaffold

B. Do not work on the first lift of the scaffold

C. Do not access the scaffold because it is incomplete or not safe

D. Do not walk under the scaffold

Answers: 10.7 = C   10.8 = A   10.9 = B   10.10 = C   10.11 = C   10.12 = C

## 10.13

 What does this sign mean?

A) No running allowed

B) There is no escape route

C) This is a fire door

D) Fire escape route

## 10.14

 What are green and white signs?

A) Mandatory signs – meaning you must do something

B) Prohibition signs – meaning you must not do something

C) Warning signs – alerting you to hazards or danger

D) Safe condition signs – giving you information

## 10.15

 What does this sign mean?

A) It tells you where the canteen is located

B) It tells you which direction to walk

C) It tells you where to assemble in case of an emergency

D) It tells you where the site induction room is located

## 10.16

 What does this sign mean?

A) Toilets and shower facilities

B) Drying area for wet weather clothes

C) Emergency first-aid shower

D) Fire sprinklers above

## 10.17

 What does this sign mean?

A) Escape route or emergency exit is to the right

B) Open the door by sliding it to the right

C) One-way pedestrian route

D) The site entrance is to the right

## 10.18

 What does this sign mean?

A) Emergency assembly point

B) Fire point

C) Accident and emergency department

D) First aid post

C
10

## 10.19

 What are yellow and black signs?

A. Mandatory signs – meaning you must do something

B. Prohibition signs – meaning you must not do something

C. Warning signs – alerting you to hazards or danger

D. Safe condition signs – giving you information

## 10.20

 What does this sign mean?

A. Risk of electrocution

B. Risk of static shock

C. Live electrical appliance

D. Risk of lightning

## 10.21

 What does this sign mean?

A. Dispose of substance or contents by burning

B. Warning – substance or contents are flammable (can catch fire easily)

C. Warning – substance or contents could explode

D. Warning – substance or contents are harmful

## 10.22

 What does this sign mean?

A. Radioactive area

B. Warning – explosive substance

C. Flashing lights ahead

D. Warning – laser beams

## 10.23

 What does this sign mean?

A. Plant operators only

B. Industrial vehicles are moving about

C. Manual handling is not allowed

D. Storage area

## 10.24

 What does this sign mean?

A. Assemble here in the event of a fire

B. Fire extinguishers and fire-fighting equipment kept here

C. Parking reserved for emergency service vehicles

D. Do not store flammable materials here

C
10

Answers: 10.19 = C   10.20 = A   10.21 = B   10.22 = D   10.23 = B  10.24 = B

# Safety signs

## 10.25

 What does this sign mean?

(A) Fire alarm call point

(B) Hot surface, do not touch

(C) Wear flameproof hand protection

(D) Emergency light switch

## 10.26

 What does this sign mean?

(A) Press here to sound the fire alarm

(B) Fire hose reel located here

(C) Turn key to open fire door

(D) Do not use if there is a fire

**C**
**10**

# 11 Fire prevention and control

## 11.1

What are **two** common fire risks on construction sites?

- A) 230 volt power tools
- B) Poor housekeeping and build up of waste
- C) Timber racks
- D) Uncontrolled hot works
- E) 110 volt extension reels

## 11.2

What is the fire assembly point?

- A) Where fire engines must go when they arrive on site
- B) Where the fire extinguishers are kept
- C) Where people must go when the fire alarm sounds
- D) Where the fire started

## 11.3

What does a fire need to burn, in addition to heat and fuel?

- A) Oxygen
- B) Carbon dioxide
- C) Argon
- D) Nitrogen

## 11.4

How would you expect to find out the location of the fire assembly point?

- A) During a visit by the Health and Safety Executive (HSE)
- B) During site induction
- C) By reading your employer's health and safety policy
- D) Your colleagues will tell you

## 11.5

If you discover a fire, what is the **first** thing you should do?

- A) Put your tools away
- B) Finish what you are doing, if it is safe to do so
- C) Try to put out the fire
- D) Raise the alarm

## 11.6

Where should you go if you hear the fire alarm?

- A) To the site canteen
- B) To the assembly point
- C) To the site office
- D) To the site welfare facilities

C
11

Answers: 11.1 = B, D   11.2 = C   11.3 = A   11.4 = B   11.5 = D   11.6 = B

## 11.7

A large fire has been reported. You have **not** been trained to use fire extinguishers. What should you do?

- A Put away all your tools and then go to the assembly point
- B Report to the site office and then go home
- C Go straight to the assembly point
- D Leave work for the day

## 11.8

How can you help to prevent a fire hazard?

- A Store solvents and paints in the drying room
- B Leave your clothes over a heater all night
- C Keep your work area tidy and place waste in the bins provided
- D Store materials and equipment along the exit routes

## 11.9

What **must** you check if you need to work in a corridor that is a fire escape route?

- A That your tools and equipment do not block the route
- B That all doors into the corridor are locked
- C That you only use spark-proof tools
- D That you remove all fire escape signs before you start

## 11.10

What does it mean if you see frost around the valve on a liquefied petroleum gas (LPG) cylinder?

- A The cylinder is nearly empty
- B The cylinder is full
- C The valve is leaking
- D You must lay the cylinder on its side

## 11.11

 A foam extinguisher, identified by a cream band, should **not** be used on what **two** types of fire?

- A Wood, paper and textile
- B Flammable liquids (fuel, oil, varnish, paints, etc.)
- C Metal and molten metal
- D Solid material
- E Electrical fires

## 11.12

 A carbon dioxide ($CO_2$) extinguisher, identified by a black band, should **not** be used on what type of fire?

- A Wood, paper, textile and solid material
- B Flammable liquids (fuel, oil, varnish, paints, etc.)
- C Electrical
- D Metal and molten metal

## 11.13

A dry powder fire extinguisher, identified by a blue band, is **best** suited to what **two** types of fire?

A) Wood, paper and textile fires

B) Flammable liquids (fuel, oil, varnish, paints, etc.)

C) Electrical fires

D) Metal fires

E) Solid material fires

## 11.14

A water fire extinguisher, identified by a red band, should **only** be used on what type of fire?

A) Wood, paper, textile and solid material

B) Flammable liquids (fuel, oil, varnish, paints, etc.)

C) Electrical

D) Metal and molten metal

## 11.15

Which two extinguishers should **not** be used on electrical fires?

A)  Dry powder (blue colour band)

B)  Foam (cream colour band)

C)  Water (red colour band)

D)  Carbon dioxide (black colour band)

## 11.16

What happens to the nozzle of a carbon dioxide ($CO_2$) fire extinguisher when it is used?

A) It gets very cold

B) It gets very hot

C) It gets very warm

D) It gets very heavy

## 11.17

What does a hot-work permit allow you to do?

A) Work in hot weather

B) Carry out work that needs warm, protective clothing

C) Carry out work that could start a fire

D) Light a bonfire

## 11.18

What does a hot-work permit **not** tell you?

A) When you can start and when you must stop the hot work

B) How you must prevent sparks or heat travelling

C) Where the local fire station is located

D) What fire extinguisher or fire watch you need

C
11

## 11.19

If your job needs a hot-work permit, what **two** things would you expect to have to do?

A Have a fire extinguisher close to the work

B Check for signs of fire when you stop work

C Know where all the fire extinguishers are kept on site

D Write a site evacuation plan

E Know how to refill fire extinguishers

## 11.20

Which **two** of these jobs are likely to need a hot-work permit?

A Cutting steel with an angle grinder

B Soldering pipework in a central heating system

C Refuelling a diesel dump truck

D Replacing an empty liquefied petroleum gas cylinder with a full one

E Using the heaters in the drying room

C
11

# 12 Electrical safety, tools and equipment

## 12.1

What **two** things should you do to reduce trips and injuries caused by untidy leads and extension cables?

A Run cables and leads above head height and over the top of doorways and walkways

B Tie any excess cables and leads up into the smallest coil possible

C Keep trailing cables and leads close to the wall

D Make sure your cables have not been used before

E Only use thinner 230 volt extension cables

## 12.2

What is the **best** way to protect an extension cable and also reduce trip hazards?

A Run the cable above head height

B Run the cable by the shortest route

C Cover the cable with yellow tape

D Cover the cable with pieces of wood

## 12.3

What **two** things **must** you do if you need to use an extension cable?

A Only uncoil the length of cable you need

B Uncoil the whole cable

C Clean the cable with a damp cloth

D Check the whole cable and connectors for damage

E Only check the part of the cable you need for damage

## 12.4

What should you do if an extension cable has a cut in its outer cover?

A Check the copper wires aren't showing in the cut and then use the cable

B Put electrical tape around the damaged part

C Report the fault and make sure no-one else uses the cable

D Put a bigger fuse in the cable plug

## 12.5

You need to work near an electric cable. The cable has bare wires. What should you do?

A Quickly touch the cable to see if it is live

B Check there are no sparks coming from the cable and then start work

C Tell your supervisor and keep well away

D Push the cable out of the way so that you can start work

C
12

### 12.6

What **two** things should you do if you need to run an electrical cable across an area used by vehicles?

- A Wrap the cable in yellow tape so that drivers can see it
- B Cover the cable with a protective ramp
- C Cover the cable with scaffold boards
- D Put up a ramp ahead sign
- E Run the cable at head height

### 12.7

Do you need to inspect simple hand tools like trowels, screwdrivers, saws and hammers?

- A No, never
- B Yes, if they have not been used for a couple of weeks
- C Yes, they should be checked each time you use them
- D Only if someone else has borrowed them

### 12.8

 What is the **main** danger of using a chisel or bolster with a mushroomed head?

- A It will shatter and send fragments flying into the air
- B You are more likely to hit your hand with the chisel head
- C The shaft of the chisel will bend, putting a strain on your wrist
- D The chisel will have a sharp, jagged edge that can cut your hand

### 12.9

What should you do if the head on your hammer comes loose?

- A Stop work and get the hammer repaired or replaced
- B Find another heavy tool to use instead of the hammer
- C Keep using it but be aware that the head could come off at any time
- D Tell the other people near you to keep out of the way

### 12.10

You are in a gang using an insulated pick to break up the surface. What **two** things should you be aware of?

- A Standing too close to the worker with the pick
- B Smoking, as gas could be released
- C Whether the ganger is watching you
- D Standing with your hands in your pockets
- E Standing in front of or behind the worker with the pick

### 12.11

Someone near you is using a rotating laser level. What is the health hazard likely to affect you?

- A Skin cancer
- B None, if used correctly they are safe
- C Gradual blindness
- D Burning of the skin, similar to sunburn

Answers: 12.6 = B, D   12.7 = C   12.8 = A   12.9 = A   12.10 = A, E   12.11 = B

## 12.12

What criteria **must** you meet to operate a power tool?

- [A] You must be over 16 years old
- [B] You must have a gold CSCS card
- [C] You must be trained and competent
- [D] You must only operate it when your supervisor is present

## 12.13

Why **must** you be fully trained before you use a cartridge-operated tool?

- [A] They are heavy and could cause manual handling injuries
- [B] They operate like a gun and can be dangerous in inexperienced hands
- [C] They can cause dermatitis when used
- [D] They have exposed electrical parts

## 12.14

What are the **two** main functions of the guards on cutting and grinding machines?

- [A] To stop materials getting onto the blade or wheel
- [B] To give you a firm handhold
- [C] To balance the machine
- [D] To stop fragments flying into the air
- [E] To stop you coming into contact with the blade or wheel

## 12.15

What should you do if the guard is missing from a power tool?

- [A] Try to make another guard
- [B] Use the tool but try to work quickly
- [C] Not use the tool until a proper guard has been fitted
- [D] Use the tool but work carefully and slowly

## 12.16

What should you do if you need to use a power tool with a rotating blade?

- [A] Remove the guard so that you can clearly see the blade
- [B] Adjust the guard to expose just enough blade to let you do the job
- [C] Remove the guard but wear leather gloves to protect your hands
- [D] Adjust the guard to expose the maximum amount of blade

## 12.17

What should you do before you adjust an electric hand tool?

- [A] Switch it off but leave the plug in the socket
- [B] Switch it off and remove the plug from the socket
- [C] You should never adjust an electric hand tool yourself
- [D] Put tape over the power switch

C
12

## 12.18

Which of the following statements about power tools is **true**?

A. Always carry the tool by its cord

B. Always unplug the tool by pulling its cord

C. Always unplug the tool when you are not using it

D. Always leave the tool plugged in when you check or adjust it

## 12.19

What should you do if the electrical equipment you are using cuts out?

A. Shake it to see if it will start again

B. Pull the electric cable to see if it is loose

C. Switch the power off and on a few times

D. Switch off the power and look for signs of damage

## 12.20

You are using a power drill when the fuse blows. A colleague shows you how to wrap the old fuse in silver foil to keep it working. What does this mean?

A. Your boss will be pleased because you can finish the job

B. The drill is dangerous and could harm you

C. You don't need to worry about the fuse blowing again

D. It is safe to carry on working

## 12.21

You need to use an air-powered tool. What **three** hazards are likely to affect you?

A. Electric shock

B. Hand-arm vibration

C. Airborne dust and flying fragments

D. Leaking hoses

E. Radiation

## 12.22

Someone near you is using a disc cutter to cut concrete blocks. What **three** immediate hazards are likely to affect you?

A. Flying fragments

B. Dermatitis

C. Harmful dust in the air

D. High noise levels

E. Vibration white finger

## 12.23

You have been asked to dig to expose power cables. You have been given a cable avoiding tool (CAT) to detect them but you haven't been shown how to use it. What should you do?

A. Dig the hole without it

B. Ask a colleague to show you how to use it

C. Read the manual before you start work

D. Tell your supervisor you haven't been trained

C
12

## 12.24

Why is it dangerous to run an abrasive wheel faster than its recommended top speed?

A The wheel will get clogged and stop

B The motor could burst into flames

C The wheel could shatter into many pieces

D The safety guard cannot be used

## 12.25

You have been asked to use a hand tool or power tool on site. You know that it is the right tool for the job. What else **must** you check?

A That it was made in the UK

B That it is inspected at the start of each week

C That it was bought from a builder's merchant

D That it is inspected before you use it

## 12.26

When do you need to check tools and equipment for damage?

A Each time before use

B Every day

C Once a week

D At least once a year

## 12.27

What **two** main visual inspections should you carry out before using a power tool?

A Check the carry case isn't broken

B Check the power lead, plug and casing are in good condition

C Check the manufacturer's label hasn't come off

D Check switches, triggers and guards are adjusted and work correctly

E Check it is marked with a security stamp

## 12.28

What does the portable appliance testing (PAT) label on a power tool tell you?

A If the inspection schedule has been monitored and reviewed

B When the tool was made

C Who tested the tool before it left the factory

D Its earth-loop impedance

## 12.29

Why should you **never** store batteries loose in your tool bag?

A You might forget to charge them

B Your tool bag will be heavy and damage your back

C If the terminals short out, they could cause a fire

D They give off a poisonous gas in a confined space

C
12

Answers: 12.24 = C   12.25 = D   12.26 = A   12.27 = B, D   12.28 = A   12.29 = C

## 12.30

Why should you try to use battery-powered tools rather than electrical ones?

- [A] They are cheaper to run
- [B] They will not give you an electric shock
- [C] They will not give you hand-arm vibration
- [D] They do not need to be tested or serviced

## 12.31

What is the recommended safe voltage for electrical equipment on building sites?

- [A] 12 volts
- [B] 24 volts
- [C] 110 volts
- [D] 230 volts

## 12.32

Why do building sites use a 110 volt electricity supply instead of a 230 volt domestic supply?

- [A] It is cheaper
- [B] It is less likely to kill you
- [C] It moves faster along the cables
- [D] It is safer for the environment

## 12.33

What colour is a 110 volt power cable and connector?

- [A] Black
- [B] Red
- [C] Blue
- [D] Yellow

## 12.34

Why should you use a RCD (residual current device) with 230 volt tools?

- [A] It lowers the voltage
- [B] It quickly cuts off the power if there is a fault
- [C] It makes the tool run at a safe speed
- [D] It saves energy and lowers costs

## 12.35

How do you check if a RCD (residual current device) connected to a power tool is working?

- [A] Switch the tool on and off
- [B] Press the test button on the RCD
- [C] Use a hand-held RCD test meter
- [D] Run the tool at top speed to see if it cuts out

C
12

Answers: 12.30 = B   12.31 = C   12.32 = B   12.33 = D   12.34 = B   12.35 = B

## 12.36

You need to use a 230 volt item of equipment. How should you protect yourself from an electric shock?

- A  Use a generator
- B  Put up safety screens around you
- C  Use a portable RCD (residual current device)
- D  Wear rubber boots and gloves

## 12.37

When is it safe to work close to an overhead power line?

- A  If you do not touch the line for more than 30 seconds
- B  If you use a wooden ladder
- C  If the power is switched off
- D  If it is not raining

C
12

## 12.38

You are using a generator to power some lighting when the lamp blows. You have a spare lamp, what should you do?

- A  Disconnect the lighting from the generator before replacing the lamp
- B  Wait for an electrician with a NICEIC card
- C  Replace the lamp without disconnecting the generator, as you can't get a shock from it
- D  Carry on working in the dark

Answers: 12.36 = C    12.37 = C    12.38 = A

# 13 Site transport safety and lifting operations

## 13.1

What are the **two** conditions for being able to operate plant on site?

- A You must be trained and competent
- B You must be authorised
- C You must be over 21 years old
- D You must hold a full driving licence
- E You must hold a British passport

## 13.2

Your supervisor asks you to drive a dumper truck. You have never driven one before. What should you do?

- A Ask a trained driver how to operate it
- B Tell your supervisor that you are not trained so cannot operate it
- C Watch other dumpers to see how they are operated
- D Get on with it

## 13.3

How would you expect to be told about the site traffic rules?

- A During site induction
- B By a Health and Safety Executive (HSE) inspector
- C By a note on a noticeboard
- D In a letter sent to your home

## 13.4

How would you expect a well-organised site to keep pedestrians away from traffic routes?

- A The site manager will direct all pedestrians away from traffic routes
- B The traffic routes will be shown on the Health and Safety Law poster
- C There will be barriers between traffic and pedestrian routes
- D There is no need to keep traffic and pedestrians apart

## 13.5

When is a site vehicle **most** likely to injure pedestrians?

- A While reversing
- B While lifting materials onto scaffolds
- C While tipping into an excavation
- D While digging out footings

## 13.6

Why must you **not** walk behind a lorry when it is reversing?

- A Most lorries are not fitted with mirrors
- B The driver is unlikely to know you are there
- C Most lorry drivers aren't very good at reversing
- D You will need to run, not walk, to get past it in time

**13.7**

The quickest way to your work area is through a contractor's vehicle compound. Which way should you go?

A Around the compound if vehicles are moving

B Straight through the compound if no vehicles appear to be moving

C Around the compound every time

D Straight through the compound if no-one is looking

**13.8**

When is site transport allowed to drive along a pedestrian route?

A During meal breaks

B If it is the shortest route

C Only if necessary and if all pedestrians are excluded

D Only if the vehicle has a flashing yellow light

**13.9**

Which of these would you **not** expect to see if site transport is well organised?

A Speed limits

B Barriers to keep pedestrians away from mobile plant and vehicles

C Pedestrians and mobile plant using the same routes

D One-way systems

**13.10**

A forklift truck is blocking the way to where you want to go on site. It is lifting materials onto a scaffold. What should you do?

A Only walk under the raised load if you are wearing a safety helmet

B Catch the driver's attention and then walk under the raised load

C Start to run so that you are not under the load for very long

D Wait or go around, but never walk under a raised load

**13.11**

When you walk across the site, what is the **best** way to avoid an accident with mobile plant?

A Keep to the designated pedestrian routes

B Ride on the plant

C Get the attention of the driver before you get too close

D Wear hi-vis clothing

**13.12**

You need to walk past a 360° mobile crane. The crane is operating near a wall. What is the **main** danger?

A The crane could crash into the wall

B You could be crushed if you walk between the crane and the wall

C You could get whole body vibration from the crane

D Your hearing could be damaged by high noise levels from the crane

C
13

## 13.13

You are walking across the site. A large mobile crane reverses across your path. What should you do?

A  Help the driver to reverse

B  Start to run so that you can pass behind the reversing crane

C  Pass close to the front of the crane

D  Wait or find another way around the crane

## 13.14

What should you do if you need to walk past someone using a mobile crane?

A  Guess what the crane operator will do next and squeeze by

B  Try to catch the attention of the crane operator

C  Run to get past the crane quickly

D  Take another route so that you stay clear of the crane

## 13.15

When can a mobile plant operator let people ride in, or on the machine?

A  Only if they have a long way to walk

B  As long as the site speed limit is not exceeded

C  Only if it is designed to carry passengers and has a designated seat

D  Only if the cab door is shut

## 13.16

You think some mobile plant is operating too close to where you have to work. What should you do **first**?

A  Stop work and speak to the plant operator

B  Stop work and speak to the plant operator's supervisor

C  Look out for the plant and carry on working

D  Stop work and speak to your own supervisor

## 13.17

What should you do if you see a dumper being driven too fast?

A  Keep out of its way and report it

B  Try to catch the dumper and speak to the driver

C  Report it to the police

D  Do nothing as dumpers are allowed to go above the site speed limit

## 13.18

You see a lorry parking. It has a flat tyre. Why should you tell the driver?

A  The lorry will use more fuel

B  The lorry will need to travel at a much slower speed

C  The lorry could be unsafe to drive

D  The lorry can only carry small loads

C
13

## 13.19

An excavator has just stopped work. Liquid is dripping and forming a small pool under the back of the machine. What could this mean?

- A  It is normal for fluids to vent after the machine stops
- B  The machine is hot so the diesel has expanded and overflowed
- C  Someone put too much diesel into the machine before it started work
- D  The machine has a leak and could be unsafe

## 13.20

You see a driver refuelling an excavator. Most of the diesel is spilling onto the ground. What is the **first** thing you should do?

- A  Tell your supervisor the next time you see them
- B  Tell the driver immediately
- C  Look for a spillage kit immediately
- D  Do nothing, as the diesel will eventually seep into the ground

## 13.21

You think a load is about to fall from a moving forklift truck. What should you do?

- A  Keep clear but try to warn the driver and others in the area
- B  Run alongside the machine and try to hold on to the load
- C  Run and tell your supervisor
- D  Sound the nearest fire alarm bell

## 13.22

A lorry is in trouble as it tries to reverse into a tight space. You have not been trained as a signaller. What should you do?

- A  Stay well out of the way
- B  Help the driver by giving hand signals
- C  Help the driver by jumping up into the cab
- D  Offer to adjust the mirrors on the lorry

## 13.23

A truck has to tip materials into a trench. Who should give signals to the truck driver?

- A  Anyone who is wearing a hi-vis coat
- B  Someone standing in the trench
- C  Someone who knows the signals
- D  Only the person who is trained and appointed for the job

## 13.24

You see a mobile crane lifting a load. The load is about to hit something. What should you do?

- A  Go and tell your supervisor
- B  Try and warn the person supervising or banking the lift
- C  Go and tell the crane driver
- D  Do nothing and assume everything is under control

C
13

## 13.25

A crane has to do a difficult lift. The signaller asks you to help, but you are not trained in plant signals. What should you do?

- A  Politely refuse and explain you don't know how to signal
- B  Start giving signals to the crane driver
- C  Only help if the signaller really can't manage alone
- D  Ask the signaller to show you what signals to use

## 13.26

What do you need before you can supervise any lift using a crane?

- A  A mobile phone so you can talk to the crane driver
- B  You must be trained and assessed as competent
- C  Written instructions from the crane hire company
- D  Nothing, the crane driver will tell you what to do

## 13.27

Which document **must** be supplied by a hire company when it delivers plant or equipment?

- A  A delivery note
- B  A repair or damage information sheet
- C  A hazardous information sheet
- D  Operator instruction information

# D

# High risk activities

**Contents**

# 14 Working at height

## 14.1

Which type of accident kills the most construction workers?

- A Falling from height
- B Contact with electricity
- C Being run over by site transport
- D Being hit by a falling object

## 14.2

How is working at height usually defined?

- A Working 1.2 m above the ground or higher
- B Working 2 m above the ground or higher
- C Working 3 m above the ground or higher
- D Working at any height that would cause an injury if you fell

## 14.3

What are **two** of your responsibilities when working at height?

- A Ensure you are sufficiently trained
- B Make use of access equipment
- C Throw things to your colleague below
- D Ignore the safety briefing given by your supervisor
- E Climb up the outside of the scaffolding

## 14.4

What should you do if you feel that a task working at height is unsafe?

- A Carry on working and tell your supervisor when you next see them
- B Work the problem out for yourself
- C Stop working immediately and report it to your supervisor
- D Borrow some work equipment from another job

## 14.5

You are required to use access equipment that you have not been trained to use. What should you do?

- A Do the job if it won't take long
- B Get a ladder instead
- C Stop work and speak to your supervisor
- D Ask someone else to do it

## 14.6

What is the **main** regulation that controls the use of suitable access equipment for working at height?

- A HSG33 Health and Safety in Roofwork
- B Lifting Operations and Lifting Equipment Regulations
- C Work at Height Regulations
- D Workplace (Health, Safety and Welfare) Regulations

**D**
14

Answers: 14.1 = A   14.2 = D   14.3 = A, B   14.4 = C   14.5 = C   14.6 = C

## 14.7

When **can** you use a ladder at work?

A If it is long enough

B You must never use a ladder on site

C If other people do not need to use it for access

D If you are doing light work for a short time

## 14.8

When using a leaning ladder what should the slope or angle of the ladder be?

A 45°

B 60°

C 75°

D 85°

## 14.9

Who should check a ladder before it is used?

A The person who is going to use it

B A supervisor

C The site safety officer

D The manufacturer

## 14.10

What is the **best** way to make sure that a ladder is secure and won't slip?

A Tie it at the top

B Ask someone to stand with their foot on the bottom rung

C Tie it at the bottom

D Wedge the bottom of the ladder with blocks of wood

## 14.11

What **must** you do when you are climbing a ladder?

A Have three points of contact with the ladder at all times

B Have two points of contact with the ladder at all times

C Use a safety harness

D Have two people on the ladder at all times

## 14.12

Why should a ladder **never** be painted?

A The paint will make the rungs slippery

B The paint may hide any damaged parts

C The paint could damage the metal parts of the ladder

D It will need regular re-painting

**D**
14

Answers: 14.7 = D   14.8 = C   14.9 = A   14.10 = A   14.11 = A   14.12 = B

## 14.13

How many people should be on a ladder at the same time?

- A One
- B Two
- C One on each section of an extension ladder
- D Three, if it is long enough

## 14.14

What should you do if you find a ladder that is damaged?

- A Don't use it and make sure that others know about the damage
- B Don't use it and report the damage at the end of your shift
- C Try to mend the damage
- D Use the ladder if you can avoid the damaged part

## D 14
## 14.15

Which of the following is **not** true when using podium steps?

- A The wheels must be locked before you get on to them
- B Podiums can easily topple if you over reach sideways
- C Podiums are safe and can't topple over
- D Podiums are work equipment and must be inspected every seven days

## 14.16

You need to use a ladder to get to a scaffold platform. Which of these statements is **true**?

- A It must be tied and extend either 1 m or five rungs above the platform
- B All broken rungs must be clearly marked
- C It must be wedged at the bottom to stop it slipping
- D Two people must be on the ladder at all times

## 14.17

What is the right way to reach the working platform of a mobile tower scaffold?

- A Climb up the tower frame on the outside of the tower
- B Lean a ladder against the tower and climb up that
- C Climb up the ladder built into the tower
- D Climb up the outside of the diagonal bracing

## 14.18

A mobile tower scaffold must **not** be used on what surface?

- A Soft or uneven ground
- B A paved patio
- C An asphalt road
- D A smooth concrete path

Answers: 14.13 = A   14.14 = A   14.15 = C   14.16 = A   14.17 = C   14.18 = A

## 14.19

You need to use a mobile tower scaffold. The wheel brakes do not work. What should you do?

A Use some wood to wedge the wheels and stop them moving

B Do not use the tower

C Only use the tower if the floor is level

D Get someone to hold the tower while you use it

## 14.20

When is it acceptable to allow someone to operate a mobile elevating work platform (MEWP) using ground-level controls?

A If the person on the ground is a trained operator and the person on the MEWP is not

B If the person in the MEWP needs both hands free to carry out the job

C If the person in the MEWP has to jump off to gain access to the work

D If the person in the MEWP cannot operate it due to an emergency

## 14.21

When working in a mobile elevating work platform (MEWP) where should you attach your harness's lanyard?

A To the control box

B To a point on the structure or building you are working on

C To the MEWP handrail

D To the designated anchor point within the platform or basket

## 14.22

If you have to work at height over or near to deep water, which item of personal protective equipment (PPE) **must** you wear?

A Wellington boots

B Lifejacket

C Full face respirator

D Full body harness

## 14.23

What should you do if you notice your harness or attachment is damaged?

A Stop and tell your supervisor straight away

B Put the harness on, use it, and plan to tell your supervisor at the end of the day

C Swap it with a colleague's harness and use theirs instead

D Stop and tell your supervisor but carry on using it until it is replaced

**D**
**14**

## 14.24

When is it safe to cross a fragile roof?

A If you walk along the line of the bolts

B If you can see fragile roof signs

C If you do not walk on any plastic panels

D If you use crawling boards with handrails

Answers: 14.19 = B   14.20 = D   14.21 = D   14.22 = B   14.23 = A   14.24 = D

## 14.25

 What does this sign mean?

A Load-bearing roof – you can stand on the surface but not on any roof lights

B Fragile roof – take care when walking on roof surface

C Fragile roof – do not stand directly on the roof and use fall protection measures

D Load-bearing roof – the surface can be slippery when wet

## 14.26

What is the **best** way to stop people falling through voids, holes or fragile roof panels?

A Tell everyone where the dangerous areas are

B Use secure covers that can take the weight of a person and add warning signage

C Cover them with netting

D Mark the areas with red and white tape

## 14.27

You are working on a flat roof. What is the **best** way to stop yourself falling over the edge?

A Put a large warning sign at the edge of the roof

B Ask someone to watch you and shout when you get too close to the edge

C Protect the edge with a guard-rail and a toe-board

D Use red and white tape to mark the edge

## 14.28

Who should erect, dismantle or alter a tube and fitting scaffold?

A Anyone who thinks they can do it

B Anyone who has the right tools

C Anyone who is trained, competent and authorised

D Anyone who is a project manager

## 14.29

What is the maximum recommended gap between the scaffold and the structure. Please select **two** answers.

A As small as possible

B No greater than 225 mm

C No greater than 300 mm

D No greater than 470 mm

E No greater than 600 mm

**D 14**

## 14.30

How do you identify the safe load rating for a scaffold platform?

A) Ask the site manager

B) Ask the telehandler driver

C) The safe load is breached when the ledgers start to deflect

D) Refer to the handover certificate or signage

## 14.31

If you store materials on a working platform, which statement is **correct**?

A) Materials can be stored unsecured above the guard-rail height

B) Materials must be stored so they can't fall and the platform must be able to take their weight

C) Materials can be stored anywhere, even if they pose a trip hazard or block the walkway

D) Materials do not need to be secured if they are going to be there for less than an hour

## 14.32

What is the **best** way to protect people below a scaffold from falling tools and materials?

A) Make sure they are wearing safety helmets

B) Tell them you will be working above them

C) Use brick guards to stop any items falling below

D) Tell the people below to stop work and clear the area

## 14.33

You need to stack materials on a working platform. What is the **best** way to stop them falling over the toe-board?

A) Fit brick guards or netting to the edge

B) Put a warning sign on the stack

C) Build the stack so that it leans away from the edge

D) Cover the stack with polythene

## 14.34

A scaffold guard-rail **must** be removed to allow you to carry out a survey. You are not a scaffolder. Can you remove the guard-rail?

A) Yes, if you put it back as soon as you have finished

B) Yes, if you put it back before you leave site

C) No, only a scaffolder can remove the guard-rail but you can put it back

D) No, only a scaffolder can remove the guard-rail and put it back

D
14

# 15 Excavations and confined spaces

## 15.1

What must happen each time a shift starts work in an excavation?

A. Someone must go in and sniff the air to see if it is safe

B. A competent person must inspect the excavation

C. A supervisor should stay in the excavation for the first hour

D. A supervisor should watch from the top for the first hour

## 15.2

When should an excavation be battened back or stepped?

A. If it is more than 5 m deep

B. If there is water in the bottom of the trench

C. If there is a risk of the sides falling in, regardless of depth

D. If any buried services cross the excavation

## 15.3

What do guard-rails around the top of an excavation prevent?

A. Toxic gases collecting in the bottom of the trench

B. People falling into the trench and being injured

C. The sides of the trench collapsing

D. Rain water running off the ground at the top and into the trench

## 15.4

What is the safest way to get into a deep excavation?

A. Climb down a secured ladder

B. Use the buried services as steps

C. Climb down the shoring

D. Use a fixed staircase

## 15.5

What should you do if you see the side supports move when you are working in an excavation?

A. Keep watching to see if they move again

B. Make sure that you and others get out quickly

C. Do nothing as the sides move all the time

D. Work in another part of the excavation

## 15.6

Why is it important that people are trained before they are allowed into a confined space?

A. Confined spaces never contain breathable air

B. The conditions inside a confined space may be harmful to health

C. Confined spaces are only found on house-building sites

D. Confined spaces always contain flammable or explosive gases

Answers: 15.1 = B   15.2 = C   15.3 = B   15.4 = D   15.5 = B   15.6 = B

## 15.7

Work in a confined space usually needs a risk assessment, a method statement and what other safety document?

A. A permit to enter

B. An up to date staff handbook

C. A written contract for the work

D. A company health and safety policy

## 15.8

What should you do if the permit to work runs out before you finish working in a confined space?

A. Carry on working until the job is finished

B. Hand the permit over to the next shift

C. Ask your supervisor to change the date on the permit

D. Leave the confined space before the permit runs out

## 15.9

You have to work in a confined space. There is no rescue team or rescue plan. What should you do?

A. Assume that a rescue team or plan is not necessary and do the job

B. Get someone to stand at the opening with a rope

C. Do not enter until a rescue plan and team are in place

D. Carry out the job in short spells

## 15.10

What is the main reason for having a person positioned immediately outside a confined space whilst work is taking place inside it?

A. To supervise the work inside the confined space

B. To check compliance with the method statement

C. To start the rescue plan if there is an emergency

D. To carry out a risk assessment for the work

## 15.11

What is the main cause of people dying while working in a confined space?

A. The presence of methane gas

B. Lack of oxygen

C. Cold conditions leading to hypothermia

D. Too much oxygen

**D**
**15**

## 15.12

What might happen if the level of oxygen drops below 8% in a confined space?

A. Your hearing could be affected

B. There is a high risk of fire or explosion

C. You could become unconscious

D. You might get dehydrated

Answers: 15.7 = A   15.8 = D   15.9 = C   15.10 = C   15.11 = B   15.12 = C

## 15.13

Before work starts in a confined space, how should the air be checked?

A Someone should go in and sniff the air

B The air should be tested with a monitor

C Someone should look around to see if there is toxic gas

D The air should be tested with a match to see if it stays alight

## 15.14

What should you do if you are in a confined space when the gas alarm sounds?

A Switch off the alarm

B Get out of the confined space immediately

C Carry on working but do not use electrical tools

D Carry on working but take plenty of breaks in the fresh air

## 15.15

You are in a deep trench and start to feel dizzy. What should you do?

A Get out, let your head clear and then go back in again

B Carry on working and hope that the feeling will go away

C Make sure that you and any others get out quickly and report it

D Sit down in the trench and take a rest

## 15.16

What **two** things should you do before entering a confined space that has sludge at the bottom?

A Identify what the sludge is

B Throw something into the sludge to see how deep it is

C Put on a disposable face mask before you go in

D Have the correct training and put on respiratory protective equipment (RPE) before you go in

E Put on a pair of wellington boots

## 15.17

Give **two** reasons why methane gas is dangerous in confined spaces.

A It can explode

B It makes you hyperactive

C You will not be able to see because of the dense fumes

D It makes you dehydrated

E You may not have enough oxygen to breathe

## 15.18

You are working in a confined space when you notice the smell of bad eggs. What is this a sign of?

A Hydrogen sulphide

B Oxygen

C Methane

D Carbon dioxide

**D**
15

## 15.19

You need to walk through sludge at the bottom of a confined space. Which of these is **not** a hazard?

A. Leptospirosis

B. The release of toxic gases

C. Slips and trips

D. The release of flammable gases

## 15.20

You are in a deep trench. A lorry backs up to the trench and the engine is left running. What should you do?

A. Put on ear defenders to cut out the engine noise

B. Ignore the problem, the lorry will soon drive away

C. See if there is a toxic gas meter in the trench

D. Get out of the trench quickly

## 15.21

When digging, you notice the soil gives off a strange smell. What is this likely to mean?

A. The soil contains a lot of clay

B. The soil has been excavated before

C. The ground has been used to grow crops in the past

D. The ground could be contaminated

## 15.22

Which of these is the most accurate way to confirm the presence of buried services?

A. Cable plans

B. Trial holes

C. Survey drawings

D. Architect drawings

## 15.23

What equipment **must** you use to hand dig near electrical underground services?

A. A jack hammer

B. An insulated spade or shovel

C. A pick and fork

D. An excavator

## 15.24

When digging you find a run of coloured marker tape. What does it mean?

A. There are buried human remains and you must tell your supervisor

B. There is a buried service and further excavation must be carried out with care

C. The soil is contaminated and you must wear respiratory protective equipment (RPE)

D. The excavation now needs side supports

**D**
**15**

## 15.25

According to the guidance on underground service pipes, what does a yellow service pipe carry?

[A] Water

[B] Gas

[C] Electricity

[D] Telecoms

## 15.26

When digging, you hit and damage a buried cable. What should you do?

[A] Move the cable out of the way and carry on digging

[B] Wait 10 seconds and then move the cable out of the way

[C] Do not touch the cable, stop work and report it

[D] Dig round the cable or dig somewhere else

**D**
15

# E

# Environment

**Contents**

# 16 Environmental awareness and waste control

## 16.1

Under environmental law, which statement is **true**?

A Only directors can be prosecuted if they do not follow the law

B Only companies can be prosecuted if they do not follow the law

C Only employees can be prosecuted if they do not follow the law

D Companies and employees can be prosecuted if they do not follow the law

## 16.2

Which **three** of the following statements are reasons why saving energy is important?

A It helps reduce energy and fuel bills

B It means energy companies can charge more for their services

C It helps to reduce the impact of climate change caused by burning fossil fuels

D It allows us to increase energy use on other sites

E It helps to save declining natural resources used to create energy

## 16.3

What are **three** of the best ways of helping to save energy on site and reduce harmful emissions?

A Switching off plant and equipment including generators when they are not in use

B Using a generator rather than mains electricity for small items of equipment

C Reporting any defective equipment so that it can be repaired and replaced

D Keeping windows and doors closed in welfare facilities when the heating is on

E Using air-powered equipment rather than mains powered equipment

## 16.4

Do you have any responsibility for minimising the amount of waste created?

A Only if you are told to do so during your site induction

B Yes, everyone on site has a responsibility to do this

C No, it is the responsibility of site management

D Only during the site clean up at the end of the project

E
16

## 16.5

Which **two** actions could help minimise waste?

- A Reuse off-cuts (such as half bricks) as far as possible, rather than discarding them
- B Use new materials at the beginning of each day
- C Leave bags of cement and plaster out in the rain, unprotected
- D Only take or open what you need and return or reseal anything left over
- E Always take much more than required – just in case you need it

## 16.6

Which of the following activities is **not** good practice on site?

- A Switching off plant and equipment when it is not in use
- B Refuelling carefully to avoid spills
- C Storing materials safely
- D Burning waste

## 16.7

What are the **two** main reasons why different types of waste should be separated on site?

- A The waste will take up less room in a skip
- B It is generally more cost effective to dispose of segregated waste
- C So the client can check what is being thrown away
- D So the wastes can be used or recycled more easily
- E To make sure the labourer has enough work to do

## 16.8

How should you get rid of hazardous waste?

- A If the waste has a hazardous symbol on it, then it can be put in any skip on site
- B Place it in the correctly labelled container or ask your supervisor
- C Put it only in a mixed waste skip
- D Take it to the nearest local authority waste tip

## 16.9

Which **two** of the following should be classed as hazardous waste?

E
16

- A Broken ceramic tiles or bricks
- B Polythene and shrink wrap
- C Glass
- D Fluorescent light tubes
- E Used spill kit pads containing oil

Answers: 16.5 = A, D   16.6 = D   16.7 = B, D   16.8 = B   16.9 = D, E

## 16.10

Which of the following should be disposed of as hazardous waste?

- A Softwood timber off-cuts
- B Glass fibre insulation
- C Part full tins of oil-based paint
- D Damaged hard hat

## 16.11

  What does this sign mean?

- A Harmful
- B Toxic
- C Corrosive
- D Harmful to the environment

## 16.12

  When a product has either of these labels, how should you dispose of the container or any residue?

- A Put it in any skip or bin
- B Follow specific instructions on the label or in work instructions
- C If it is a liquid and less than one litre you can pour it down a drain
- D Leave it somewhere for other people to deal with

## 16.13

You are on site and need to throw away some waste liquid that has oil in it. What should you do?

- A Pour it down a drain or sink in the welfare facilities
- B Pour it slowly onto the ground and let it soak away
- C Pour it into a sealed container and put it into a general waste skip
- D Ask your supervisor or environmental advisor how to get rid of it

## 16.14

What should you do if there is an oil or diesel spill on site?

- A Ignore it, oil or diesel spills do not have serious long-term effects
- B Stop work, contain the spill, notify your supervisor and then clean up the spill
- C Call the Department for the Environment immediately, so they can arrange to have it cleaned up
- D Use a spill kit to clean it up before the end of the day

E
16

## 16.15

You have been asked to clean up oil that has leaked from machinery onto the ground. What is the right way to do this?

A  Put the oily soil into the general waste skip

B  Put the oily soil into a separate container for collection as hazardous waste

C  Mix the soil up with other soil so that the oil cannot be seen

D  Wash the oil away with water and detergent

## 16.16

Which of the following is **not** good practice on site?

A  Creating a nuisance to the residents of neighbouring properties

B  Preventing water and soil pollution

C  Saving energy

D  Minimising the amount of waste created in doing a job

## 16.17

Which of the following would **not** be classed as causing a nuisance to a site's neighbours?

A  Carefully directed site lighting

B  Noise and vibration from construction activities

C  Lorries and heavy plant approaching and leaving the site

D  Dust and fumes from site

## 16.18

You are carrying out a noisy work activity and realise that it cannot be finished within the normal working hours of your site. What is the **first** thing you should do?

A  Carry on so that you can finish doing the job as soon as possible

B  Stop work and inform site management so they can look at the impact of working hours

C  Visit your site's neighbours to tell them what you will be doing

D  Ensure you are wearing appropriate hearing protection before you resume work

## 16.19

You notice that a detail can't be built in the way it has been designed. What should you do?

A  Keep quiet as it will mean more work for you

B  Raise the issue with your supervisor before you start work

C  Use your experience and build it as you think it should be done

D  Leave that detail out altogether

E
16

## 16.20

You discover a bird on a nest where you need to work. What should you do?

A  Cover it with a bucket

B  Move it, do your work and then put it back

C  Make others aware of its presence whilst you go and inform your supervisor

D  Scare it away

## 16.21

You would like to store a pallet of bricks in a space under a tree, what should you do?

A  Place them there as they will not be in the way

B  Only place them there if they will not be damaged by passing vehicles

C  Only place them there if you can avoid damaging your vehicle or branches

D  Do not place them there, as compaction of the soil over the roots can damage the tree

## 16.22

What should you do if the heaters are on and the site cabins are too hot inside?

A  Open the windows or doors

B  Nothing

C  Turn down the heaters

D  Remove some clothing

## 16.23

While excavating you notice some interesting old coins in the loosened soil. What should you do?

A  Stop digging and contact your supervisor

B  Keep digging and see how many more you can find

C  Hide them. Archaeologists working on site will hold up works

D  Keep quiet, you found them so you can keep them

E
16

# Congratulations

# You have now completed the core knowledge questions

## For the operatives' test

You still need to prepare for the behavioural case studies, which you can do by:

⊕ watching the film *Setting out* at www.citb.co.uk/settingout

▣ reading the transcript of the film at the back of this book.

## For the specialists' test

You should now revise the appropriate specialist activity from Section F.

You then need to prepare for the behavioural case studies, which you can do by:

⊕ watching the film *Setting out* at www.citb.co.uk/settingout

▣ reading the transcript of the film at the back of this book.

# F

## Specialist activities

### Contents

If you are preparing for a specialist test you also need to revise the appropriate specialist activity, from those listed below.

## 17 Supervisory

### 17.1

When the Construction (Design and Management) Regulations 2015 apply, what must be in place before construction work begins?

A   The health and safety file

B   The construction phase plan

C   The method statement

D   A construction contract agreement

### 17.2

Under the Construction (Design and Management) Regulations 2015, where would you find the arrangements for managing health and safety for the project you are working on?

A   In the health and safety file

B   In the construction phase plan

C   In the contract documentation

D   In the designer's risk assessment

### 17.3

Under the Construction (Design and Management) Regulations 2015, what must be provided before construction work starts, and then maintained until the end of the project?

A   A safety log book

B   A premises log book

C   A car park or other parking facilities

D   Adequate welfare facilities

### 17.4

Under the Construction (Design and Management) Regulations 2015, which **two** of the following must you ensure workers have received before they start working on site?

A   A suitable site induction, specific to the work

B   Details of the client's brief and project expectations

C   Confirmation of their working hours and rest breaks

D   Details of the designer's plan of work

E   Information on relevant hazards and control measures

### 17.5

How long must you keep inspection records on site under the Construction (Design and Management) Regulations 2015?

A   For three months after the inspection has been carried out

B   For one week on site before sending them to head office

C   Until the project is completed and then for three months

D   At the site until the project is completed

F
17

## 17.6

Under the Construction (Design and Management) Regulations 2015, when the contractor sets a person to work on a construction site, what must they ensure that person has, or be in the process of obtaining?

A  The right skills, knowledge, training and experience

B  A relevant competency card

C  Hard hat, hi-vis and safety footwear

D  A relevant qualification for the work to be undertaken

## 17.7

Under the Construction (Design and Management) Regulations 2015, which of the following must be in place before demolition work can start?

A  A construction phase safety plan

B  The arrangements for demolition recorded in writing

C  A demolition risk assessment

D  A pre-tender demolition health and safety plan

## 17.8

What is the purpose of the health and safety file that is handed to the client at the end of the project?

A  To help people who have to carry out work on the structure in the future

B  To help prepare the final accounts for the structure

C  To record the health and safety standards of the structure

D  To record the accident statistics of the construction project

## 17.9

Which piece of equipment is used with a cable avoidance tool (CAT) to detect cables?

A  Compressor

B  Signal generator

C  Metal detector

D  Gas detector

## 17.10

In the colour coding of electrical power supplies on site, what voltage does a blue plug represent?

A  50 volts

B  110 volts

C  230 volts

D  415 volts

F
17

Answers: 17.6 = A   17.7 = B   17.8 = A   17.9 = B   17.10 = C

## 17.11

On the site electrical distribution system, which colour plug indicates a 415 volt supply?

A Yellow

B Blue

C Black

D Red

## 17.12

Why **must** a RCD (residual current device) be used in conjunction with 230 volt electrical equipment?

A It lowers the voltage

B It quickly cuts off the power if there is a fault

C It makes the tool run at a safe speed

D It saves energy and lowers costs

## 17.13

How could a site worker check if the RCD (residual current device) through which a 230 volt hand tool is connected to the supply is working correctly?

A Switch the tool on and off

B Press the test button on the RCD unit

C Switch the power on and off

D Run the tool at top speed to see if it cuts out

## 17.14

When working near, but **not** underneath, overhead lines, how far should the safety zone extend from either side of the overhead line?

A 3 m

B 4 m

C 5 m

D 6 m

## 17.15

Where should an escape route or routes ensure safe access to?

A The ground

B The open air

C A place of safety

D The first-aid room

## 17.16

Which of the following tasks would you expect the appointed person to carry out if someone is injured?

A They should provide most of the care normally carried out by a first aider

B They should provide all of the care normally carried out by a first aider

C They should contact the emergency services

D They should only apply splints to broken bones

F
17

## 17.17

What does the proactive monitoring of health and safety procedures involve?

A) Ensuring that staff always do the work that they have been instructed to do safely

B) Deciding how to prevent accidents similar to those that have already occurred

C) Looking at the work to be done, what could go wrong and how it could be done safely

D) Checking that all staff read and understand all health and safety notices

## 17.18

Why may a young person be more at risk of having an accident?

A) Legislation does not apply to anyone under 18 years of age

B) They are usually left to work alone to gain experience

C) They have less experience and may not recognise danger or understand fully what could go wrong

D) They are less likely to wear personal protective equipment (PPE)

## 17.19

In which regulations will you find the details of the welfare facilities that **must** be provided on site?

A) The Control of Substances Hazardous to Health (COSHH)

B) The Construction (Design and Management) Regulations

C) The Management of Health and Safety at Work Regulations

D) The Workplace (Health, Safety and Welfare) Regulations

## 17.20

Which **two** of the following factors **must** be considered when providing first-aid facilities on site?

A) The cost of first-aid equipment

B) The hazards, risks and nature of the work carried out

C) The number of people expected to be on site at any one time

D) The difficulty in finding time to purchase the necessary equipment

E) The space in the site office to store the necessary equipment

F
17

## 17.21

What does a COSHH assessment tell you?

- [A] How to lift heavy loads and how to protect yourself
- [B] How to work safely in confined spaces
- [C] How to use a substance safely in the environment it is to be used
- [D] How to assess noise levels to protect your hearing

## 17.22

You have to use a new material for the **first** time and need to carry out a COSHH assessment. What are the **two** main things you will need?

- [A] Your company's safety policy
- [B] The material safety data sheet
- [C] The age of the people doing the work
- [D] The material delivery note
- [E] Details of where, who and how you will be using the product

## 17.23

When does an employer have to prepare a written health and safety policy?

- [A] If they employ five people or more
- [B] If they employ three people or more
- [C] If they employ a safety officer
- [D] If the work is going to last more than 30 days

## 17.24

If there is a fatal accident or a reportable dangerous occurrence on site, when **must** the Health and Safety Executive (HSE) be informed?

- [A] Immediately
- [B] Within five days
- [C] Within seven days
- [D] Within ten days

## 17.25

The significant findings of risk assessments **must** be recorded when more than a certain number of people are employed. How many?

- [A] Three or more
- [B] Five or more
- [C] Six or more
- [D] Seven or more

## 17.26

What **must** happen if a prohibition notice is issued by an inspector of the Health and Safety Executive (HSE) or local authority?

- [A] Work can continue, as long as a risk assessment is carried out
- [B] The work that is subject to the notice must cease
- [C] The work can continue if extra safety precautions are taken
- [D] The work in hand can be completed, but no new works started

## 17.27

Who should you inform if someone tells you that they have work-related hand-arm vibration syndrome (HAVS)?

A) The Health and Safety Executive (HSE)

B) The local Health Authority

C) Their doctor

D) The nearest hospital

## 17.28

In deciding what control measures to take, following a risk assessment that has revealed a risk, what measure should you always consider **first**?

A) Make sure personal protective equipment (PPE) is available

B) Adapt the work to the individual

C) Give priority to measures that protect the whole workforce

D) Avoid the risk altogether if possible

## 17.29

In considering what measures to take to protect people against risks to their health and safety, how should you regard personal protective equipment (PPE)?

A) As the first line of defence

B) As the only practical measure

C) As the best way to tackle the job

D) As the first option, as long as it is used in conjunction with collective protection

## 17.30

In the context of a risk assessment, what does the term risk mean?

A) Something with the potential to cause harm or injury

B) An unsafe act or condition

C) The likelihood that a hazard could cause harm or injury

D) Any work activity that can be described as dangerous

## 17.31

If a sub-contracted worker is 17 years old, what **must** the employer provide them with?

A) A mentor or buddy to stay with them at all times

B) Health and Safety Executive (HSE) permission for the 17-year-old to be on site

C) The legal guardian's permission for the 17-year-old to be on site

D) A risk assessment addressing the issue of young persons

## 17.32

From a safety point of view, which of the following should be considered **first** when deciding on the number and location of access and egress points to a site?

A) Off road parking for cars and vans

B) Access for the emergency services

C) Access for heavy vehicles

D) Site security

F
17

Answers: 17.27 = A   17.28 = D   17.29 = D   17.30 = C   17.31 = D   17.32 = B       **105**

## 17.33

What is the purpose of using a permit to work system?

A To ensure that the job is being carried out quickly

B To ensure that the job is carried out by the easiest method

C To enable tools and equipment to be properly checked before work starts

D To establish a controlled, safe system of work

## 17.34

What is the **best** way for a supervisor or manager to make sure that the operatives doing a job have fully understood a method statement?

A Put the method statement in a labelled spring-binder in the office

B Explain the method statement to those doing the job and test their understanding

C Make sure that those doing the job have read the method statement

D Display the method statement on a noticeboard in the office

## 17.35

Why is it important that hazards are identified?

A They have the potential to cause injury or harm

B They must all be eliminated before work can start

C They must all be notified to the Health and Safety Executive (HSE)

D So that toolbox talks can be given on the hazards

## 17.36

Before planning for anyone to enter a confined space, what should be the **first** consideration of the manager or supervisor who is following the principles of prevention?

A Has the atmosphere in the confined space been tested

B Has a safe means of access and egress been established

C Is there an alternative method of doing the work

D Have all who intend to enter the confined space been properly trained

F
17

Answers: 17.33 = D   17.34 = B   17.35 = A   17.36 = C

## 17.37

When is it advisable to take precautions to prevent people, plant or materials falling into an excavation?

A At all times

B When the excavation is 2 m or more deep

C When the excavation is 1.2 m or more deep

D When there is a risk from an underground cable or other service

## 17.38

Which of the following precautions should be taken to prevent a dumper that is tipping material into an excavation from falling into it?

A Dumpers should be kept 5 m away from the excavation

B Stop blocks should be provided parallel to the trench, and appropriate to the vehicle's wheel size

C Dumper drivers are required to judge the distance carefully or be given stop signals by another person

D Cones or signage should be erected to indicate the safe tipping point

## 17.39

When planning possible work in a confined space, what should be the **first** consideration?

A How long the job will take

B How to avoid the need for operatives to enter the space

C How many operatives will be required

D What personal protective equipment (PPE) will be needed

## 17.40

Which of the following is a significant hazard when excavating alongside a building or structure?

A Undermining or weakening the foundations of the building

B Noise and vibration affecting the occupiers of the building

C Excavating too deeply into soft ground

D Damage to the surface finish of the building or structure

## 17.41

What danger is created by excessive oxygen in a confined space?

A Increase in breathing rate of workers

B Increased flammability of combustible materials

C Increased working time inside work area

D False sense of security

F
17

## 17.42

How should cylinders containing liquefied petroleum gas (LPG) be stored on site?

- A In a locked cellar with clear warning signs
- B In a locked cage at least 3 m from any oxygen cylinders
- C Within a secure storage container at the back of the site
- D Covered by a tarpaulin to shield the compressed cylinder from sunlight

## 17.43

Where should liquefied petroleum gas (LPG) cylinders be positioned when supplying an appliance in a site cabin?

- A Inside the cabin in a locked cupboard
- B Under the cabin
- C Inside the cabin next to the appliance
- D Outside the cabin

## 17.44

What should be the capacity of a spillage bund in a fuel storage tank, in addition to the volume of content of the tank?

- A 10% (110% of the total content)
- B 30% (130% of the total content)
- C 50% (150% of the total content)
- D 75% (175% of the total content)

## 17.45

Which of the following should be considered to prevent exposure to hazardous substances?

- A What instruction, training and supervision to provide
- B What health surveillance arrangements will be needed
- C How to minimise risk and control exposure
- D How to monitor the exposure of workers in the workplace

## 17.46

Before allowing a lifting operation to be carried out, where **must** you record the sequence of operations to enable a safe lift?

- A In the crane hire contract
- B In an approved lifting plan or method statement
- C In a lifting operation toolbox talk
- D In a risk assessment

## 17.47

Where **must** the number of people who may be carried in a passenger hoist on site be displayed?

- A It should be displayed on a legible notice in the site welfare area
- B It should be displayed on a legible notice within the cage of the hoist
- C It should be included in the site induction
- D It should be explained to the hoist operator

Answers: 17.42 = B   17.43 = D   17.44 = A   17.45 = C   17.46 = B   17.47 = B

## 17.48

How should access be controlled, if people are working in a riser shaft?

A. By a site security operative

B. By those who are working in it

C. By the main contractor

D. By a permit to work system

## 17.49

What is regarded as the last resort in the hierarchy of control for operatives' safety when working at height?

A. Safety harness

B. Mobile elevating work platform (MEWP)

C. Mobile tower scaffold

D. Access tower scaffold

## 17.50

When do the Work at Height Regulations require a working platform to be inspected by a competent person?

A. After an accident

B. Every day

C. Fortnightly

D. Before first use and then every seven days thereafter

## 17.51

What is the advantage of using safety nets rather than harness and lanyard?

A. Safety nets do not need inspecting

B. Workers' lanyards can get entangled with other workers' lanyards

C. Safety nets provide collective fall protection

D. Safety nets can be rigged by anyone

## 17.52

What should be included in a method statement for working at height? Give **three** answers.

A. The cost of the job and time it will take

B. The sequence of operations and the equipment to be used

C. How much insurance cover will be required

D. How falls are to be prevented

E. Who will supervise the job on site

## 17.53

When putting people to work above public areas, what should be your **first** consideration?

A. To minimise the number of people below at any one time

B. To prevent complaints from the public

C. To let the public know what you are doing

D. To prevent anything falling on to people below

F
17

## 17.54

What **must** edge protection be designed to do?

(A) To allow persons to work on both sides of it

(B) To secure tools and materials close to the edge

(C) To warn people where the edge of the roof is

(D) To prevent people and materials from falling

## 17.55

The Beaufort Scale is important when working at height externally. What does it measure?

(A) It measures air temperature

(B) It measures the load-bearing capacity of a flat roof

(C) It measures wind speed

(D) It measures the load-bearing capacity of a scaffold

## 17.56

Why is it dangerous to use inflatable airbags for fall arrest if they are too big for the area to be protected?

(A) They will exert a sideways pressure on anything that is containing them

(B) The pressure in the bags will cause them to burst

(C) The inflation pump will become overloaded

(D) They will not fully inflate

## 17.57

If a scaffold is **not** complete, which of the following actions should be taken by the supervisor?

(A) Make sure that the scaffolders complete the scaffold

(B) Tell all operatives not to use the scaffold

(C) Display a warning notice and tell operatives to use the scaffold with care

(D) Prevent access to the scaffold and add warning signage

## 17.58

Following a scaffold inspection under the Work at Height Regulations, how soon **must** a report be given to the person on whose behalf the inspection was made?

(A) Within two hours

(B) Within six hours

(C) Within 12 hours

(D) Within 24 hours

## 17.59

What is the **minimum** height of the main guard-rail on a scaffold?

(A) 875 mm

(B) 910 mm

(C) 950 mm

(D) 1,000 mm

F
17

Answers: 17.54 = D   17.55 = C   17.56 = A   17.57 = D   17.58 = D   17.59 = C

## 17.60

On a scaffold, what **must** be the largest unprotected gap between any guard-rail, toe-board, barrier or other similar means of protection?

A) 400 mm

B) 470 mm

C) 500 mm

D) 600 mm

## 17.61

Which of the following is a fall-arrest system?

A) Guard-rail and toe-board

B) Scaffold towers

C) Mobile elevating work platform (MEWP)

D) Safety harness and lanyard

## 17.62

Under the requirements of the Work at Height Regulations, what **must** the minimum width of a working platform be?

A) Suitable and sufficient for the job in hand

B) Two scaffold boards wide

C) Three scaffold boards wide

D) Four scaffold boards wide

## 17.63

For a fixed ladder, what is the maximum vertical height that may be climbed before an intermediate landing place is required?

A) 7.5 m

B) 8 m

C) 8.5 m

D) 9 m

## 17.64

What should you do if you notice that operatives working above a safety net are dropping off-cuts of material and other debris into the net?

A) Nothing, as the debris is all collecting in one place

B) Ensure that the net is cleared of debris weekly

C) Have the net cleared and inspected, then ensure it is not allowed to happen again

D) Ensure that the net is cleared of debris daily

## 17.65

When **must** a competent person routinely inspect a working platform?

A) After it is erected and at intervals not exceeding seven days

B) Only after it has been erected

C) After it is erected and then at monthly intervals

D) After it is erected and then at intervals not exceeding 10 days

F
17

## 17.66

Ideally, where should a safety net be rigged?

A Immediately below where you are working

B 2 m below where you are working

C 6 m below where you are working

D At any height below the working position

## 17.67

What is the **main** danger of leaving someone who has fallen suspended in a harness for too long?

A The anchorage point may fail

B They may try to climb back up the structure and fall again

C They may suffer loss of consciousness or fatal injury

D It is a distraction for other workers

## 17.68

When should guard-rails be fitted to a working platform?

A If it is possible to fall 2 m

B At any height if a fall could result in an injury

C If it is possible to fall 3 m

D Only if materials are being stored on the working platform

## 17.69

A design feature of some airbags used for fall arrest is a controlled leak rate. If you are using these, what **must** you ensure about the inflation pump?

A It must be electrically powered

B It must be switched off from time to time to avoid over-inflation

C It must run all the time while work is carried out at height

D It must be switched off when the airbags are full

## 17.70

What is your **least** reliable source of information when assessing the level of vibration from a powered, hand tool?

A In-use vibration measurement of the tool

B Vibration figures taken from the tool manufacturer's handbook

C Your own judgement based upon observation or experience

D Vibration data from the Health and Safety Executive's (HSE) master list

F
17

## 17.71

What does the term lower exposure action value (80 decibels (dBA)) mean, when referring to noise?

A  The average background noise level

B  The noise level at which the worker can request hearing protection

C  The level of noise which must not be exceeded on the site boundary which causes noise nuisance

D  The noise level at which the worker must wear hearing protection

## 17.72

At what decibel (dBA) level does it become mandatory for an employer to establish hearing protection zones?

A  80 decibels (dBA)

B  85 decibels (dBA)

C  90 decibels (dBA)

D  95 decibels (dBA)

## 17.73

At what minimum noise level **must** you provide hearing protection to workers if they ask for it?

A  80 decibels (dBA)

B  85 decibels (dBA)

C  87 decibels (dBA)

D  90 decibels (dBA)

## 17.74

What is the significance of a weekly or daily personal noise exposure of 87 decibels (dBA)?

A  It is the lower action value and no action is necessary

B  It is the upper action value and hearing protection must be issued

C  It is the peak sound pressure and all work must stop

D  It is the exposure limit value and must not be exceeded

## 17.75

Electric welding is about to start on your site. What should be used to protect passers-by from getting arc eye?

A  Warning signs

B  Screens

C  Personal protective equipment (PPE)

D  Nothing

F
17

Answers: 17.71 = B   17.72 = B   17.73 = A   17.74 = D   17.75 = B

# 18 Demolition

## 18.1

If asbestos is present what should happen before demolition or refurbishment takes place?

- A) Advise workers that asbestos is present then continue with demolition
- B) All asbestos should be removed as far as reasonably practicable
- C) Advise the Health and Safety Executive (HSE) that asbestos is present and continue with demolition
- D) Inspect the condition of the asbestos materials

## 18.2

What kind of survey is required to identify asbestos prior to demolition?

- A) Type 3 survey
- B) Management survey
- C) Refurbishment and demolition survey
- D) Type 2 survey

## 18.3

Who **must** be the **first** person a demolition contractor appoints before undertaking demolition operations?

- A) A competent person to supervise the work
- B) A sub-contractor to strip out the buildings
- C) A safety officer to check on health and safety compliance
- D) A quantity surveyor to price the extras

## 18.4

If there are any doubts about a building's stability, who should a demolition contractor consult?

- A) Another demolition contractor
- B) A structural engineer
- C) A Health and Safety Executive (HSE) factory inspector
- D) The company safety adviser

## 18.5

Which of the following pieces of equipment can a 17-year-old trainee demolition operative use unsupervised?

- A) Excavator 360°
- B) Dump truck
- C) Wheelbarrow
- D) Rough terrain forklift

F
18

## 18.6

When would it be unsafe to operate a scissor lift?

A) If the controls on the platform are used

B) If the ground is soft and sloping

C) If weather protection is not fitted

D) If the machine is low on fuel

## 18.7

On site, what is the minimum distance that oxygen should be stored away from propane, butane or other gases?

A) 1 m

B) 2 m

C) 3 m

D) 4 m

## 18.8

Where should liquefied petroleum gas (LPG) cylinders be located when being used for heating or cooking in site cabins?

A) Under the kitchen area work surface

B) Inside but near the door for ventilation

C) In a nearby storage container

D) Securely outside the cabin

## 18.9

What type of fire extinguisher should **not** be provided where petrol or diesel is being stored?

A) Foam

B) Water

C) Dry powder

D) Carbon dioxide

## 18.10

What is most likely to be caused by continual use of hand-held breakers or drills?

A) Dermatitis

B) Weil's disease (leptospirosis)

C) Vibration white finger

D) Skin cancer

## 18.11

What is the **most** common source of high levels of lead in the blood of operatives doing demolition work?

A) Stripping lead sheeting

B) Cutting lead-covered cable

C) Cold cutting fuel tanks

D) Hot cutting coated steel

F
18

Answers: 18.6 = B   18.7 = C   18.8 = D   18.9 = B   18.10 = C   18.11 = D

## 18.12

Which **one** of the following items of personal protective equipment (PPE) provides the lowest level of protection when working in dusty conditions?

- [A] Half-mask dust respirator
- [B] Positive pressure-powered respirator
- [C] Compressed airline breathing apparatus
- [D] Self-contained breathing apparatus

## 18.13

Which **one** of the following would be suitable to use when cutting coated steelwork?

- [A] A disposable dust mask
- [B] Positive pressure-powered respirator
- [C] High-efficiency dust respirator
- [D] A nuisance dust mask

## 18.14

After exposure to lead, what precautions should you take before eating or drinking?

- [A] Wash your hands and face
- [B] Do not smoke
- [C] Change out of dirty clothes
- [D] Rinse your mouth with clean water

## 18.15

Where is the **only** place you will **not** find information about the daily checks required for mobile plant?

- [A] On the stickers attached to the machine
- [B] In the manufacturer's handbook
- [C] In the supplier's information
- [D] On the Health and Safety Law poster

## 18.16

What should you do while reversing mobile plant if you lose sight of the signaller or slinger who is directing you?

- [A] Carry on reversing slowly
- [B] Stop the vehicle
- [C] Adjust your wing mirror
- [D] Sound the horn and move forward

## 18.17

How often should lifting equipment, which is **not** used to lift people, be thoroughly examined?

- [A] Every six months
- [B] Every two years
- [C] A maximum of every 12 months
- [D] Every 14 months

**F**
18

Answers: 18.12 = A   18.13 = B   18.14 = A   18.15 = D   18.16 = B   18.17 = C

## 18.18

What should you do when leaving mobile plant unattended?

- A Leave the engine running, if safe to do so
- B Park it in a safe place, remove the keys and lock it
- C Put the parking brake on and tell people not to use it
- D Put a sign saying no unauthorised access on it

## 18.19

Which statement is **true** with regard to using machines?

- A Guards can be removed to make work easier
- B It's OK to wear rings and other jewellery as long as you take care
- C You can carefully remove waste material while the machine is in motion
- D Never use a machine unless you have been trained and given permission to use it

## 18.20

Which of the following is **not** a part of a plant operator's daily pre-use check?

- A Emergency systems
- B Engine oil level
- C Hydraulic fluid level
- D Brake pad wear

## 18.21

Which of these statements is **true** in relation to an operator of a scissor lift?

- A They must be trained and authorised in the use of the equipment
- B They must only use the ground level controls
- C They must be in charge of the work team
- D They must ensure that only one person is on the platform at any time

## 18.22

On demolition sites, what **must** the drivers of plant have, for their own and others' safety?

- A Adequate visibility from the driving position
- B A temperature controlled cab
- C Wet weather gear when it's raining
- D A supervisor in the cab with them

## 18.23

When **must** head and tail lights be used on mobile plant?

- A If the plant is using the same traffic route as private cars
- B When the plant is operating in conditions of poor visibility
- C When the plant is operated by a trainee
- D Only if the plant is crossing pedestrian routes

F
18

Answers: 18.18 = B    18.19 = D    18.20 = D    18.21 = A    18.22 = A    18.23 = B          **117**

# Demolition

## 18.24

What safety feature is provided by FOPS on mobile plant?

- A The speed is limited when tracking over hard surfaces
- B The machine stops automatically if the operator lets go of the controls
- C The operator is protected from falling objects
- D The reach is limited when working near to live overhead cables

## 18.25

What should you do if you discover underground services **not** previously identified?

- A Fill in the hole immediately
- B Stop work until the situation has been resolved
- C Cut the pipe or cable to see if it's live
- D Get the machine driver to dig it out

## 18.26

What action should you take if you discover unlabelled drums or containers on site?

- A Put them in the nearest waste skip
- B Ignore them. They will get flattened during the demolition
- C Stop work until they have been safely dealt with
- D Open them and smell the contents to see if they are flammable

## 18.27

The plant you are driving has defective brakes. What action should you take?

- A Reduce your speed
- B Report it and carry on working
- C Report it and isolate the machine
- D Use the handbrake instead of the foot brakes until the machine is fixed

## 18.28

What action should be taken if a wire rope sling is defective?

- A Do not use it and make sure that no-one else can
- B Only use it for up to half its safe working load
- C Report the defect at the end of the day
- D Only use it for small lifts under 1 tonne

## 18.29

Which **two** of the following documents refer to the specific hazards associated with demolition work in confined spaces?

- A Safety policy
- B Permit to work
- C Risk assessment
- D Scaffolding permit
- E Hot-work permit

F
18

## 18.30

When asbestos material is suspected in buildings to be demolished, what is the **first** priority?

A Ensure a competent person carries out an asbestos survey

B Notify the Health and Safety Executive (HSE) of the possible presence of asbestos

C Remove and dispose of the asbestos

D Employ a licensed asbestos remover

## 18.31

What is the **safest** method of demolishing brick or internal walls by hand?

A Undercut the wall at ground level

B Work across in even courses from the ceiling down

C Work from the doorway at full height

D Cut down at corners and collapse in sections

## 18.32

Who should be consulted before demolition is carried out near to overhead cables?

A The Health and Safety Executive (HSE)

B The fire service

C The electricity supply company

D The land owner

## 18.33

When demolishing a building in controlled sections, what is the **most** important consideration for the remaining structure?

A The soft strip is completed

B All non-ferrous metals are removed

C It remains stable

D Trespassers cannot get in at night

## 18.34

Where would you find out the intended method for controlling identified hazards on a demolition project?

A The demolition toolbox

B The demolition plan

C The pre-tender health and safety plan

D The construction phase health and safety plan

## 18.35

How **must** cans or drums be stored, to prevent any leakage from spreading?

A On wooden pallets off the ground

B On their sides and chocked to prevent movement

C Upside down to prevent water penetrating the screw top

D In a bund

F
18

Answers: 18.30 = A   18.31 = B   18.32 = C   18.33 = C   18.34 = B   18.35 = D

## 18.36

When hinge-cutting a steel building or structure for a controlled collapse, which should be the last cuts?

A Front leading row top cuts

B Front leading row bottom cuts

C Back row top cuts

D Back row bottom cuts

## 18.37

What safety devices should be fitted between the pipes and the gauges of oxy-propane cutting equipment?

A Non-return valves

B On-off taps

C Flame retardant tape

D Flashback arresters

## 18.38

What type of fire extinguisher should you **not** use in confined spaces?

A Water

B Carbon dioxide

C Dry powder

D Foam

## 18.39

What should be obtained before carrying out the demolition cutting of fuel tanks?

A A gas free certificate

B An isolation certificate

C A risk assessment

D A COSHH assessment

## 18.40

How long is a gas free certificate issued for?

A One hour

B 24 hours

C One week

D One month

## 18.41

What do the letters SWL stand for?

A Satisfactory working limit

B Safe working level

C Satisfactory weight limit

D Safe working load

## 18.42

Which of the following is **true** in relation to the safe working load of a piece of equipment?

A It must never be exceeded

B It is a guide figure that may be exceeded slightly

C It may be exceeded by 10% only

D It gives half the maximum weight to be lifted

## 18.43

What should be clearly marked on all lifting gear?

A Date of manufacture

B Name of maker

C Date next test is due

D Safe working load

F
18

Answers: 18.36 = D   18.37 = D   18.38 = B   18.39 = A   18.40 = C   18.41 = D
18.42 = A   18.43 = D

## 18.44

How often should lifting accessories be thoroughly examined?

A Every three months

B Every six months

C Every 14 months

D Every 18 months

## 18.45

How often do operators need to inspect plant and equipment and record the details? Please select **two** answers.

A At the beginning of each shift

B Daily

C Weekly

D Monthly

E Every three months

## 18.46

What is the importance of having ROPS fitted to some mobile plant?

A It ensures that the tyre pressure is correct

B It protects the operator if the machine rolls over

C It prevents over-pressurisation of the hydraulic system

D It prevents unauthorised passengers being carried

## 18.47

What is the correct way to climb off a machine?

A Jump down from the seated position

B Climb down, facing forward

C Climb down, facing the machine

D Use a ladder

## 18.48

When is it acceptable to carry passengers on a machine?

A When the employer gives permission

B When they are carried in the skip

C When the machine is fitted with a purpose-made passenger seat

D When the maximum speed is no greater than 10 mph

## 18.49

With regard to the safe method of working, what is the **most** important subject of induction training for demolition operatives?

A Working hours on the site

B Explanation of the method statement

C Location of welfare facilities

D COSHH assessments

F
18

# 19  Highway works

## 19.1

Why is it **not** safe to use diesel to prevent asphalt sticking to the bed of lorries?

A  It will create a slipping hazard

B  It will corrode the bed of the lorry

C  It will create a fire hazard

D  It will react with the asphalt, creating explosive fumes

## 19.2

You are moving or laying slabs, paving blocks or kerbs on site. Which **two** of the following methods would be classed as manual handling?

A  Using a scissor lifter attachment on an excavator

B  Using a trolley or sack barrow

C  Using a suction lifter attached to an excavator

D  Using a two man scissor lifter

E  Using a crane with fork attachment

## 19.3

What are **two** effects of under-inflated tyres on the operation of a machine?

A  It decreases the operating speed of the engine

B  It can make the machine unstable

C  It causes increased tyre wear

D  It decreases tyre wear

E  It increases the operating speed of the engine

## 19.4

If you are driving any plant that may overturn, when **must** a seatbelt be worn?

A  When travelling over rough ground

B  When the vehicle is loaded

C  When you are carrying passengers

D  At all times

## 19.5

What precautions should be taken when parking on a gradient with the front of the vehicle pointing down the hill?

A  Switch the engine off and turn wheels onto full lock

B  Apply the handbrake, switch the engine off and remove the key

C  Leave the engine running and park crosswise

D  Apply the handbrake and put chocks under the wheels

## 19.6

If the dead man's handle on a machine does **not** operate, what should you do?

A  Keep quiet in case you get the blame

B  Report it at the end of the shift

C  Try and fix it or repair it yourself

D  Stop and report it immediately to your supervisor

F
19

## 19.7

When can you carry authorised passengers in vehicles?

A) Only if your supervisor gives you permission

B) Only if a suitable secure seat is provided for each of them

C) Only when off the public highway

D) Only if you have a full driving licence

## 19.8

When it is necessary to tip into an excavation, what is the preferred method of preventing the vehicle getting too close to the edge?

A) Signage

B) Driver's experience

C) Signaller

D) Stop-blocks

## 19.9

Which of these is the safest method of operating a machine under electrical power lines when it has an extending jib or boom?

A) Erect signs to warn drivers while they are operating the machines

B) Adapt the machines to limit the extension of the jib or boom

C) Place a warning notice on the machine

D) Let down the tyres on the machine to increase the clearance

## 19.10

When using lifting equipment, such as a cherry picker, lorry loader or excavator, how should you follow the indicated safe working load?

A) It must never be exceeded

B) It is a guide figure that may be exceeded slightly

C) It may be exceeded by 10% only

D) It gives half the maximum weight to be lifted

## 19.11

Which checks should the operator of a mobile elevating work platform (MEWP), for example a cherry picker, carry out before using it?

A) That a seatbelt is provided for the operator

B) That a roll-over cage is fitted

C) That the hydraulic system is drained

D) That emergency systems operate correctly

## 19.12

A single vehicle is being used to carry out mobile highway works during the day. What sign or symbol **must** be clearly displayed on or at the rear of the vehicle?

A) Road narrows sign (left or right)

B) A specific task warning sign (for example, gully cleaning)

C) A keep left or right arrow

D) A roadworks ahead sign

F
19

Answers: 19.7 = B   19.8 = D   19.9 = B   19.10 = A   19.11 = D   19.12 = C

## 19.13

When should you switch on the amber flashing beacon fitted to your highways vehicle?

A At all times

B When travelling to and from the depot

C When it is being used as a works vehicle

D Only in poor visibility

## 19.14

What **must** you do approximately 200 m before a site works access on a motorway?

A Switch on the vehicle hazard lights

B Switch on the flashing amber beacon

C Switch on the headlights

D Switch on the flashing amber beacon and the appropriate indicator

## 19.15

How often **must** a competent person thoroughly examine lifting equipment for carrying persons, for example a cherry picker?

A Every six months

B Every 12 months

C Every 18 months

D Every 24 months

## 19.16

What **must** you do before towing a trailer fitted with independent brakes?

A Fit a safety chain

B Fit a cable that applies the trailer's brakes if the tow hitch fails

C Use a rope to secure the trailer to the tow hitch

D Make sure it is possible to drive at a maximum speed of 25 mph along the route you have chosen

## 19.17

What **must** you do when getting off plant and vehicles?

A Use a pair of steps which allow you to climb out of the vehicle

B Use the wheels and tyres for access

C Use the designated access and egress point whilst maintaining three points of contact with the vehicle

D Look before you jump, then jump down facing the vehicle

## 19.18

What should you do when leaving plant unattended?

A Leave the amber flashing beacon on

B Apply the brake, switch off engine and remove the key

C Leave it in a safe place with the engine ticking over

D Park with blocks under the front wheels

F
19

## 19.19

What **must** you have before towing a compressor on the highway? Give **two** answers.

- A  Permission from your supervisor
- B  The correct class of driving licence
- C  Permission from the police
- D  Permission from the compressor hire company
- E  Working lights and a number plate on the compressor that matches that of the towing machine

## 19.20

Who is responsible for the security of the load on a vehicle?

- A  The driver's supervisor
- B  Police
- C  The driver
- D  The driver's company

## 19.21

What is the correct way to dismount from the cab or driving seat of plant and vehicles?

- A  Use three points of contact facing forwards (away from the vehicle)
- B  Jump down facing forwards (away from the vehicle)
- C  Use three points of contact facing backwards (towards the vehicle)
- D  Jump down well clear of the vehicle

## 19.22

Why is it necessary to wear hi-vis clothing when working on roads?

- A  So that road users and plant operators can see you
- B  So that your supervisor can see you
- C  To protect clothes worn underneath from damage
- D  Because it will keep you warm

## 19.23

You are working on a dual carriageway with a 60 mph speed limit although you are **not** in the working space. What is the minimum standard of hi-vis clothing that you **must** wear?

- A  Reflective waistcoat
- B  Reflective long-sleeved jacket
- C  Reflective sash
- D  Reflective hard hat

## 19.24

When working on the highway, when does hi-vis personal protective equipment (PPE) clothing give you maximum protection?

- A  When it is tied around your waist
- B  When it is worn open to flap in the wind
- C  When it is worn over other garments and fastened at the front
- D  When it is soiled and very dirty

F
19

## 19.25

When kerbing works are being carried out, how should kerbs be taken off the vehicle?

A By lifting them off manually using the correct technique

B By pushing them off the back

C By using mechanical means, such as a JCB fitted with a grab

D By asking your workmate to give you a hand

## 19.26

What is the purpose of an on-site risk assessment?

A To ensure there is no risk of traffic build-up due to the works in progress

B To identify hazards and risks specific to the site in order to ensure a safe system of work

C To ensure that the work can be carried out in reasonable safety

D To protect the employer from prosecution

## 19.27

In which **two** places would you find information about the distances for setting out highways signs in advance of the works under different road conditions?

A In the Traffic Signs Manual (Chapter 8)

B In the Pink Book

C On the back of the sign

D In the specification for highway works

E In the new Code of Practice (Red Book)

## 19.28

You are the driver of a vehicle and lose sight of the signaller while reversing your vehicle. What do you do?

A Continue reversing slowly

B Continue reversing as long as your vehicle is equipped with a klaxon and flashing lights

C Stop and locate the signaller

D Find someone else to watch you reverse safely

## 19.29

What should you do with materials that have to be kept on site overnight?

A Don't stack them above 2 m high

B Stack them safely and in a secure area

C Put pins and bunting around them

D Only stack them on the grass verge

F
19

Answers: 19.25 = C   19.26 = B   19.27 = A, E   19.28 = C   19.29 = B

## 19.30

What **two** actions should be taken to prevent the release of harmful silica dust while mechanically cutting kerbs, slabs and blocks?

A Pump water onto the cutting disc to suppress the dust (wet cut)

B Press down on the disc cutter to finish the job faster

C No action is necessary as wind clears the dust

D Wear a correctly fitting mask with the correct dust protection factor (FFP3)

E Use a diamond blade cutting disc

## 19.31

When providing portable traffic signals on roads used by cyclists, what action should you take?

A Locate the signals at bends in the road

B Allow more time for slow-moving traffic by increasing the 'all red' phase of the signals

C Operate the signals manually

D Use 'stop and go' boards only

## 19.32

What is the **main** reason why temporary highways signing needs to be removed when works are completed?

A To get traffic flowing

B It is a legal requirement

C To allow the road to be opened fully

D To reuse signs on new jobs

## 19.33

When should installed highways signs and guarding equipment be inspected?

A Immediately after it has been used

B No more frequently than once a week

C Every hour, except when the site is unattended

D Regularly and at least once every day, including when the site is unattended

## 19.34

Which **two** site conditions **must** be met before traffic management can be reduced to the minimum requirements?

A Traffic is heavy

B Visibility is good

C There are double yellow lines

D There is a footpath

E It is a period of low risk

## 19.35

What traffic management is required when carrying out a maintenance job on a motorway?

A The same as would be required on a single carriageway

B A flashing beacon and a keep left or right sign

C A scheme installed by a registered traffic management contractor

D Ten 1 m high cones and a 1 m high men working sign

F
19

## 19.36

What is the minimum traffic management required when carrying out a short-term minor maintenance job in a quiet, low-speed side road?

- A: A flashing amber beacon and a keep left or right arrow
- B: The same as required for a road excavation
- C: Five cones and a blue arrow
- D: Temporary traffic lights

## 19.37

What is the maximum distance between the roadworks ahead signs for work activities that move along the carriageway, such as sweeping, verge mowing and road lining?

- A: Two miles
- B: One mile
- C: Half a mile
- D: Quarter of a mile

## 19.38

What action is required when a highways vehicle fitted with a direction arrow is travelling from site to site?

- A: Point the direction arrow up
- B: Travel slowly from site to site
- C: Point the direction arrow down
- D: Cover or remove the direction arrow

## 19.39

How **must** signs on footways be located?

- A: So that they block the footway
- B: So that they can be read by site personnel
- C: So that they do not create a hazard for pedestrians
- D: So that they can be easily removed

## 19.40

What should you do if drivers approaching highway works cannot see the advance signs clearly because of poor visibility or obstructions caused by road features?

- A: Place additional signs in advance of the works
- B: Extend the safety zones
- C: Extend the sideways clearance
- D: Lengthen the lead-in taper

## 19.41

How should you protect a portable traffic-light cable that crosses a road?

- A: It should be secured firmly to the road surface
- B: A cable crossing protector must be used with ramp warning signs
- C: It can be unprotected if it is less than 10 mm in diameter
- D: It should be placed in a slot cut into the road surface

F
19

## 19.42

What action is required where passing traffic may block the view of highways signs?

- A Signs must be larger
- B Signs must be duplicated on both sides of the road
- C Signs must be placed higher
- D Additional signs must be placed in advance of the works

## 19.43

How **must** highway signs, lights and guarding equipment be properly secured?

- A With built-in weights where possible
- B By roping them to concrete blocks or kerb stones
- C By pushing them securely into the soft verge
- D By iron weights suspended from the frame by chains or other strong material

## 19.44

Which is **not** an approved means of controlling traffic at roadworks?

- A Priority signs
- B Police supervision
- C Hand signals by operatives
- D A give-and-take system

## 19.45

What action is required if a vehicle detector on temporary traffic lights becomes defective?

- A Control traffic at the defective end using hand signals
- B Operate on all red and call the service engineer
- C Operate on fixed time or manual and call the service engineer
- D Switch the lights off until the supervisor arrives on site

## 19.46

How should portable traffic signals be assembled and placed?

- A As speedily as possible
- B In an organised manner to a specified sequence
- C During the night
- D As work starts each morning

## 19.47

What action is required where it is **not** possible to maintain the correct safety zone?

- A Barrier off the working space
- B Place additional advance signing
- C Use extra cones on the lead-in taper
- D Stop work and consult your supervisor

F
19

## 19.48

In which of the following circumstances can someone enter the safety zone?

A To store unused plant

B To maintain cones and signs

C To park site vehicles

D To store materials

## 19.49

On a dual carriageway, a vehicle driven by a member of the public enters the coned-off area. What action do you take?

A Remove a cone and direct the driver back on to the live carriageway

B Ignore them

C Shout and wave them off site

D Help them to leave the site safely, using the nearest designated exit

## 19.50

When working after dark, is mobile plant exempt from the requirement to show lights?

A Yes, always

B Yes, if authorised by the supervisor

C Only if they are not fitted to the machine as standard

D Not in any circumstances

## 19.51

What is the purpose of the safety zone?

A To indicate the works area

B To protect you from the traffic and the traffic from you

C To allow extra working space in an emergency

D To give a safe route around the working area

## 19.52

What should be used to protect the public from a shallow excavation in a public footway?

A Pins and bunting

B Nothing

C Cones

D Barriers with tapping rails

## 19.53

In which of the following circumstances would it **not** be safe to use a cherry picker for working at height?

A When a roll-over cage is not fitted

B When the ground is uneven and sloping

C When weather protection is not fitted

D When the operator is clipped to an anchorage point in the basket

**F**
**19**

## 19.54

Where would you find information about working on a dual carriageway with a speed limit above 40 mph?

A In the welfare cabin

B In the Blue Book

C In the Traffic Signs Manual (Chapter 8)

D In the Pink Book

## 19.55

What is **not** usually something to consider while undertaking a site-specific risk assessment before starting highway works?

A The cost of the sub-contractor who will be carrying out the work

B The amount and type of traffic

C The effect of different weather conditions

D The type and size of the road

## 19.56

When providing portable traffic signals on roads where horses are ridden, what action should you take?

A Suspend operations until the horse is clear of the works site

B Continue working as normal

C Shout at the rider to hurry up

D Close the road to make sure horses cannot use it during operations

**F**
19

Answers: 19.54 = C   19.55 = D   19.56 = A

## 20 Specialist work at height

### 20.1

If you need to store materials on a roof, what **three** things **must** you do?

A Check the load bearing capability of the roof to avoid damage to the structure

B Stack materials no more than 1.2 m above the guard-rail height

C Ensure there is safe access and clear working areas around the materials for everyone working on the roof

D Use a gin wheel and rope tied to a temporary tripod at the roof edge for raising and lowering the materials

E Store the materials in a way that prevents them from falling off or being blown off the roof

### 20.2

What should you do if a safety lanyard has damaged stitching?

A Use the lanyard if the damaged stitching is less than 5 cm long

B Get a replacement lanyard

C Not use the damaged lanyard and work without one

D Use the lanyard if the damaged stitching is less than 15 cm long

### 20.3

What is the **main** danger of leaving someone who has fallen suspended in a harness for too long?

A The anchorage point may fail

B They may try to climb back up the structure and fall again

C They may suffer severe trauma or fatal injury

D It is a distraction for other workers

### 20.4

If using inflatable airbags as a means of fall arrest, what **must** you ensure with regard to the inflation pump?

A It must be electrically powered

B It must be switched off from time to time to avoid over-inflation

C It must run all the time while work is carried out at height

D It must be switched off when the airbags are full

### 20.5

Why is it dangerous to use inflatable airbags that are too big for the area to be protected?

A They will exert a sideways pressure on anything that is containing them

B The pressure in the bags will cause them to burst

C The inflation pump will become overloaded

D They will not fully inflate

F
20

Answers: 20.1 = A, C, E   20.2 = B   20.3 = C   20.4 = C   20.5 = A

## 20.6

When is it most appropriate to use a safety harness and lanyard for working at height?

A Only when the roof has a steep pitch

B Only when crossing a flat roof with clear roof lights

C Only when all other options for fall prevention have been ruled out

D Only when materials are stored at height

## 20.7

When trying to clip your lanyard to an anchor point you find the locking device does **not** work. What should you do?

A Carry on working and report it later

B Tie the lanyard in a knot round the anchor

C Stop work and report it to your supervisor

D Carry on working without it

## 20.8

What is the **main** reason for using a safety net or other soft-landing system rather than a personal fall-arrest system?

A Soft-landing systems are cheaper to use and do not need inspecting

B It is always easier to rescue workers who fall into a soft-landing system

C Specialist training is not required to install soft-landing systems

D Soft-landing systems are collective fall arrest measures

## 20.9

What is edge protection designed to do?

A Make access to the roof easier

B Secure tools and materials close to the edge

C Stop rainwater running off the roof onto workers below

D Prevent people and materials from falling

## 20.10

What is the **maximum** permitted gap between the guard-rails on a working platform?

A 350 mm

B 470 mm

C 490 mm

D 510 mm

## 20.11

When should guard-rails be fitted to a working platform?

A If it is possible to fall 2 m

B At any height if a fall could result in an injury

C If it is possible to fall 3 m

D Only if materials are being stored on the working platform

F
20

## 20.12

The Beaufort Scale is important when working at height externally. What does it measure?

A It measures air temperature

B It measures the load-bearing capacity of a flat roof

C It measures wind speed

D It measures the load-bearing capacity of a scaffold

## 20.13

Before starting work at height, the weather forecast says the wind will increase to Force 7. What is the **best** description of the wind conditions?

A A moderate breeze that can raise light objects, such as dust and leaves

B A near gale that will make it difficult to move about and handle materials

C A gentle breeze that you can feel on your face

D Hurricane winds that will uproot trees and cause structural damage

## 20.14

You have to lean over an exposed edge while working at height. How should you wear your safety helmet?

A Tilted back on your head so that it doesn't fall off

B Take your helmet off while leaning over then put it on again afterwards

C Wear the helmet as usual but use the chinstrap

D Wear the helmet back to front whilst leaning over

## 20.15

Before climbing a ladder you notice that it has a rung missing near the top. What should you do?

A Do not use the ladder and immediately report the defect

B Use the ladder but take care when stepping over the position of the missing rung

C Turn the ladder over so that the missing rung is near the bottom and then use it

D See if you can find a piece of wood to replace the rung

## 20.16

How far should a ladder extend above the stepping-off point if there is no alternative, firm handhold?

A Three rungs

B Two rungs

C One metre

D Half a metre

F
20

## 20.17

When using portable or pole ladders for access, what is the maximum vertical distance between landings?

(A) 4 m

(B) There is no maximum

(C) 9 m

(D) 30 m

## 20.18

What is a Class 3 ladder?

(A) A ladder for domestic use only and must not be used on site

(B) An industrial quality ladder which can be used safely

(C) A ladder that has been made to a European Standard

(D) It is made of insulating material and can be used near to overhead cables

## 20.19

You need to use a ladder to access a roof. The only place to rest the ladder is on a run of plastic gutter. What **two** things should you consider doing?

(A) Resting the ladder on a gutter support bracket

(B) Resting the ladder against the gutter, climb it and quickly tie it off

(C) Finding another way to access the roof

(D) Using a proprietary stand-off device that allows the ladder to rest against the wall

(E) Position the ladder at a shallow angle so that it rests below the gutter

## 20.20

Who should erect and dismantle scaffold towers?

(A) Someone who has the instruction book

(B) Someone who is trained, competent and authorised

(C) Advanced scaffolders

(D) Someone who has worked on them before

## 20.21

What is the recommended maximum height for a free-standing mobile tower when it is used indoors?

(A) There is no restriction

(B) Three lifts

(C) The height recommended by the manufacturer

(D) Three times the longest base dimension

## 20.22

After gaining access to the platform of a mobile tower, what is the **first** thing you should do?

(A) Check that the tower's brakes are locked on

(B) Check that the tower has been correctly assembled

(C) Close the access hatch to stop people or equipment from falling

(D) Check that the tower does not rock or wobble

F
20

Answers: 20.17 = C   20.18 = A   20.19 = C, D   20.20 = B   20.21 = C   20.22 = C

## 20.23

What **must** you do before a mobile tower is moved?

- A Clear the platform of people and equipment
- B Get a permit to work
- C Get approval from the principal contractor
- D Make arrangements with the forklift truck driver

## 20.24

An outdoor tower scaffold has stood overnight in high winds and heavy rain. What should you ensure before the scaffold is used?

- A That the brakes still work
- B That the scaffold is tied to the adjacent structure
- C That the scaffold is inspected by a competent person
- D That the platform hatch still works correctly

## 20.25

What should someone working from a cherry picker attach their lanyard to?

- A A strong part of the structure you are working on
- B A secure anchorage point inside the platform
- C A secure point on the boom of the machine
- D A scaffold guard-rail

## 20.26

You are working at height from a cherry picker when the weather becomes very windy. What should your **first** consideration be?

- A Tie all lightweight objects to the handrails of the basket
- B Clip your lanyard to the structure that you are working on
- C Tie the cherry picker basket to the structure you are working on
- D Decide whether the machine will remain stable

## 20.27

You are on a cherry picker but it does not quite reach where you need to work. What should you do?

- A Use a stepladder balanced on the machine platform
- B Extend the machine fully and stand on the guard-rails
- C Abandon the machine and use a long extending ladder
- D Do not carry out the job until you have an alternative means of access

**F**
**20**

## 20.28

If you are working at height and operating a mobile elevating work platform (MEWP), when is it acceptable for someone to use the ground-level controls?

A If the person on the ground is trained and you are not

B In an emergency

C If you need to jump off the MEWP to gain access to the work

D If you need both hands free to carry out the job

## 20.29

When is it acceptable to jump off a mobile elevating work platform (MEWP) on to a high level work platform?

A If the work platform is fitted with edge protection

B If the machine operator stays in the basket

C Not under any circumstances

D If the machine is being operated from the ground-level controls

## 20.30

How will you know the maximum weight or number of people that can be lifted safely on a mobile elevating work platform (MEWP)?

A The weight limit is reached when the platform is full

B It will say on the Health and Safety Law poster

C You will be told during site induction

D From an information plate fixed to the machine

## 20.31

When is it safe to use a scissor lift on soft ground?

A When the ground is dry

B When the machine can stand on scaffold planks laid over the soft ground

C When your supervisor has assessed the ground conditions as suitable

D Never

## 20.32

You need to cross a fragile roof. How do you establish if it is fragile?

A Tread gently and listen for cracking

B Stop and seek advice

C Look at the roof surface and make your own assessment

D It does not matter if you walk along a line of bolts

F
20

Answers: 20.28 = B   20.29 = C   20.30 = D   20.31 = C   20.32 = B

## 20.33

After gaining access to a roof, you notice some overhead cables within reach. What should you do?

A Keep away from them while you work but remember that they are there

B Stop work and confirm that it is safe for you to be on the roof

C Make sure that you are using a wooden ladder

D Hang coloured bunting from them to remind you they are there

## 20.34

What should be included in a safety method statement for working at height? Give **three** answers.

A The cost of the job and time it will take

B The sequence of operations and the equipment to be used

C How much insurance cover will be required

D How falls are to be prevented

E Who will supervise the job on site

## 20.35

When it is **not** possible to avoid working above public areas, what should be your **first** consideration?

A To minimise the number of people below at any one time

B To prevent complaints from the public

C To let the public know what you are doing

D To prevent anything falling on to people below

## 20.36

What **two** requirements should roof light covers meet?

A They must be made from the same material as the roof covering

B They must be made from clear material to allow the light through

C They must be strong enough to take the weight of any load placed on them

D They must be waterproof and windproof

E They must be fixed in position to stop them being dislodged

**F**
**20**

## 20.37

Which of these **must** happen before any roof work starts?

A) A risk assessment must be carried out following the hierarchy of controls

B) The operatives working on the roof must be trained in the use of safety harnesses

C) Permits to work must be issued to those allowed to work on the roof

D) A weather forecast must be obtained

## 20.38

When working at height, which of these is the safest way to transfer waste materials to ground level?

A) Through a waste chute directly into a skip

B) Asking someone below to keep the area clear of people then throw the waste down

C) Erecting barriers around the area where the waste will land

D) Bagging or bundle up the waste before throwing it down

## 20.39

You need to inspect pipework at high level above an asbestos roof. How should you access it?

A) Use an extension ladder and crawler board to get to the pipework

B) Use a ladder to get onto the roof and walk the bolt line on the roof sheets

C) Report the pipework as unsafe

D) Hire in suitable mobile access equipment

## 20.40

You have been asked to erect specialist access frames using anchor bolts. Before you start work what should you **not** do?

A) Check the access frames are sound

B) Assume that the access system is safe to use

C) Test the anchor bolts

D) Ensure that your assistant has their harness on

## 20.41

You are working above a safety net. You notice the net is damaged. What should you do?

A) Work somewhere away from the damaged area of net

B) Stop work and report it

C) Tie the damaged edges together using the net test cords

D) See if you can get hold of a harness and lanyard

F
20

## 20.42

What is the **main** reason for not allowing debris to gather in safety nets?

A. It will overload the net

B. It looks untidy from below

C. It could injure someone who falls into the net

D. Small pieces of debris may fall through the net

## 20.43

You are working at height, but the securing cord for a safety net is in your way. What should you do?

A. Untie the cord, carry out your work and tie it up again

B. Untie the cord, but ask the net riggers to re-tie it when you have finished

C. Tell the net riggers that you are going to untie the cord

D. Leave the cord alone and report the problem

## 20.44

Ideally, where should a safety net be rigged?

A. Immediately below where you are working

B. 2 m below where you are working

C. 6 m below where you are working

D. At any height below the working position

## 20.45

Who should install safety nets?

A. A scaffolder

B. Someone who has had experience of working with them before

C. A trained, competent and authorised person

D. A steel or cladding erector

## 20.46

When can someone who is **not** a scaffolder remove parts of a scaffold?

A. Only if the scaffold is not more than two lifts in height

B. As long as a scaffolder refits the parts after the work has finished

C. Never, only competent scaffolders can remove the parts

D. Only if they think the parts won't weaken the scaffold

## 20.47

During your work, you find that a scaffold tie is in your way. What should you do?

A. Ask a scaffolder to remove it

B. Remove it yourself and then replace it when you have finished your work

C. Remove it yourself but get a scaffolder to replace it when you have finished your work

D. Report the problem to your supervisor

F
20

## 20.48

Which type of scaffold tie can be removed by someone who is **not** a scaffolder?

- A | A box tie
- B | A ring tie
- C | A reveal tie
- D | No types can be removed

F
20

## 21 Lifts and escalators

### 21.1

Who is allowed to safely release trapped passengers?

A) The site manager

B) Only a trained and authorised person

C) Anyone

D) Only the emergency services

### 21.2

How should you connect a car light supply to a 240 volt supply (240 volt fused spur)?

A) Connect it with the power on

B) Switch off the spur and then connect it

C) Switch off the spur, remove the fuse and then connect it

D) Isolate and lock off the incoming supply and then connect it

### 21.3

A switch needs to be changed in the pit but the isolator is in the machine room 12 floors above. What should you do?

A) Isolate the power and then lock and tag the isolator

B) Risk assess the situation and change the switch with the power on because it is control voltage

C) Use insulated tools

D) Stand on a rubber mat

### 21.4

What is the main cause of injury and absence for workers in the lift and escalator industry?

A) Falls

B) Electrocution

C) Contact with moving parts

D) Manual handling

### 21.5

If a counterweight screen is **not** fitted or has been removed, what should you do before starting work?

A) Carry out a further risk assessment to establish a safe system of work

B) Nothing – just get on with the job as normal

C) Give a toolbox talk on guarding

D) Issue and wear appropriate personal protective equipment (PPE)

### 21.6

Which of the following types of fire extinguisher should **not** be used if there is a fire in a lift or escalator controller?

A) Halon

B) Water

C) Dry powder

D) Carbon dioxide

F
21

Answers: 21.1 = B   21.2 = D   21.3 = A   21.4 = D   21.5 = A   21.6 = B

## 21.7

What should you do if the lifting tackle you are about to use is defective?

A) Only use it for half its safe working load

B) Only use it for small lifts under 1 tonne

C) Do not use it and inform your supervisor

D) Try to fix it

## 21.8

If landing doors are **not** fitted to a lift on a construction site, what is the **minimum** height of the barrier that must be fitted instead?

A) 650 mm

B) 740 mm

C) 810 mm

D) 950 mm

## 21.9

A set of chain blocks has been delivered to site with a certificate stating they were inspected by a competent person a month ago. The hook is obviously damaged. What action do you take?

A) Use the blocks as the certificate is current

B) Do not use the blocks and inform your supervisor

C) Use the blocks at half the safe working load

D) Use the blocks until replacement equipment arrives

## 21.10

When must you **not** wear rings, bracelets, wrist watches, necklaces and similar items?

A) When working near or on electrical or moving equipment

B) When working on site generally

C) When driving a company vehicle

D) After leaving home for work

## 21.11

What is the correct method for disposing of used or contaminated oil?

A) Decant it into a sealed container and place in a skip

B) Dispose of it through a registered waste process

C) Dilute it with water and pour it down a sink

D) Pour it down a roadside drain

## 21.12

A large, heavy, balance weight frame is delivered to site on a lorry with no crane. There is no lifting equipment available on site. What should you do?

A) Unload it manually

B) Arrange for it to be re-delivered on a suitable lorry

C) Slide it down planks

D) Tip the load off the lorry

F
21

Answers: 21.7 = C   21.8 = D   21.9 = B   21.10 = A   21.11 = B   21.12 = B

# Lifts and escalators

## 21.13

A lifting beam at the top of the lift shaft is marked with a safe working load of 800 kg but the brickwork around the beam is cracked and appears to be loose. What should you do?

A  Use the beam as normal

B  Only lift loads not exceeding 400 kg

C  Not use the beam and speak to your supervisor

D  De-rate the beam by 75%

## 21.14

What is fitted to prevent injury from an overspeed governor?

A  A rope

B  A restrictor

C  A guard

D  A switch

## 21.15

If the escalator or passenger conveyor has an external machine room, which statement applies to its access doors?

A  They should be capable of being locked from both sides and be marked with an appropriate safety sign

B  They should be smoke proof in case of a fire

C  They should be unlocked at all times in case of an emergency

D  They should be capable of being locked on the inside only and be marked with the appropriate safety sign

## 21.16

What is the statutory period of inspection for lifting equipment that is used to support people?

A  At least monthly

B  At least every six months

C  At least every 12 months

D  Once every two years

## 21.17

What checks do you need to carry out before using lifting equipment?

A  A drop check

B  That it is free from defects and has a current inspection certificate

C  That the chains are knotted to the correct length

D  That the lifting tackle states the date of manufacture

## 21.18

Following the initial inspection, how often should a scaffold in a lift shaft be inspected by a competent person?

A  At least every day

B  At least every seven days

C  At least every 14 days

D  There is no set period between inspections

F
21

## 21.19

While installing a new rope, you notice a damaged section where something heavy has fallen onto the coil. What should you do?

A  Fit the rope anyway

B  Cut out the damaged section

C  Reject the rope

D  Add an extra termination

## 21.20

What must you do **first**, before entering the pit of an operating lift?

A  Fit pit props

B  Verify the pit stop switch

C  Switch the lift off

D  Position the access ladder

## 21.21

Who should fit a padlock and tag to an electrical lock-out guard?

A  Anyone working on the unit

B  Only the engineer who fitted the lock-out device

C  Only the senior engineer

D  Only the manufacturer

## 21.22

You arrive on site and find the lift mains isolator switched off. What should you do?

A  Switch it on and get on with your work

B  Switch it on and check the safety circuits to see if there is a fault

C  Contact the person in control of the premises to find out if they had switched off the lift

D  Shout down the shaft and if no-one responds switch it on and get on with your work

## 21.23

Which **two** of the following actions must be carried out by an authorised person working alone?

A  Before starting work, registering their presence with the site representative

B  Ensuring their timesheet is accurate and countersigned

C  Establishing suitable arrangements to ensure the monitoring of their wellbeing

D  Notifying the site manager of the details of the work

E  Ensuring that the lift pit is free from water and debris

F
21

Answers: 21.19 = C   21.20 = B   21.21 = A   21.22 = C   21.23 = A, C

## 21.24

Which statement is true when using authorised lifting tackle marked with its safe working load?

A) Never exceed the safe working load

B) The safe working load is only guidance

C) Halve the safe working load if the equipment is damaged

D) Double the safe working load if people are to be lifted

## 21.25

What should be fitted to the main sheave and diverter to prevent injury from rotating equipment?

A) Movement sensors

B) Guards

C) Clutching assembly

D) Safety notices

## 21.26

What are the appropriate types of tools and equipment for working on electrical lift-control equipment?

A) Insulated tools and an insulating mat

B) Non-insulated tools

C) Any tools and an insulating mat

D) No tools are allowed near electrical equipment

## 21.27

When installing a partially enclosed or observation lift, what safe system of work can you use to prevent injury to people below?

A) Put up a sign

B) Do not use heavy tools

C) Secure tools to prevent them falling off

D) Only carry out essential work using minimum tools

## 21.28

What needs to be checked before any hot work takes place in the lift installation?

A) The weight and size of the welding equipment

B) How long the task will take

C) If a hot-work permit or permit to work is required

D) If the local fire services need to be notified

## 21.29

What must you ensure if the trapdoor or hatch has to be left open while you work in the machine room?

A) That a sign is posted to warn others that you are working there

B) That the distance from the trapdoor or hatch to the floor below does not exceed 2 m

C) That there is sufficient light available for the work

D) That a suitable barrier is put in place around the trapdoor or hatch

F
21

## 21.30

What **must** you ensure to prevent unauthorised access to unoccupied machine equipment space?

A) That the access door is locked

B) That a sign is posted to warn trespassers

C) That the power supply is isolated

D) That a person is posted to prevent access

## 21.31

What should be applied to the main isolator of a traction lift to prevent it starting accidentally?

A) A warning notice

B) A lock-out device

C) An RCD (residual current device)

D) Lower-rated fuses

## 21.32

Who is responsible for the keys when a padlock has been applied to a lock-out device?

A) The individual applying the lock

B) The site supervisor

C) The site manager

D) The person nearest the lock-out device

## 21.33

If work needs to be done on electrical lift equipment, and the main isolator does **not** have a lock-out device, what is an alternative method of isolating the supply?

A) Detach the main power supply

B) Place insulation material in the contactors

C) There is no alternative to a lock-out device for isolating the supply

D) Withdraw and retain the fuse and post notices warning that the machinery is being worked on

## 21.34

The main contractor wants to use an unfinished lift to move some equipment to an upper floor. What should you do?

A) Help to ensure the load is correctly positioned

B) Tell them to talk to your supervisor

C) Ask for the weight of the equipment

D) Allow them to use the lift but take no responsibility for any accidents

## 21.35

What is an essential action before gaining access into the escalator or passenger conveyor?

A) That the mains switch is locked and tagged out

B) That the mains switch is in the on position

C) That all steps are removed

D) That the drive mechanism is lubricated

F
21

Answers: 21.30 = A   21.31 = B   21.32 = A   21.33 = D   21.34 = B   21.35 = A    **147**

## 21.36

What is secured at the entry and exit points of an escalator or passenger conveyor to prevent people falling into the machine or machine space?

A  Safety barriers

B  Safety notices

C  Escalator machine equipment guards

D  Machine tank covers

## 21.37

What **must** you do before moving the steps or pallet band of an escalator or passenger conveyor?

A  Check that there are no sharp edges on the steps

B  Check that there is a clear route of escape

C  Check that no unauthorised people are on the equipment

D  Check that a fire extinguisher is available

## 21.38

What is the minimum size of gap between the edge of the work platform and the hoist way wall that is regarded as a fall hazard?

A  250 mm

B  300 mm

C  330 mm

D  450 mm

## 21.39

When is it acceptable to work on the top of a car without a top-of-car control station?

A  When the unit has been locked and tagged out

B  When two engineers are working on it

C  When there is no other way to work on it

D  When only one person is working on it

## 21.40

Which statement is true when working on an energised car?

A  Always attach your lanyard to the car top while standing on the landing

B  Make sure you step onto the landing with your lanyard still attached to the car

C  Always check the lanyard is unclipped before getting off the car top

D  Ensure that your lanyard is clipped to a guide bracket or similar anchorage on the shaft

**F**
**21**

## 21.41

What is the last thing you should do before getting off a car top through open landing doors when the car-top control is within 1 m of the landing threshold?

A) Set the car-top control to test

B) Ensure that the car-top stop button is set to stop and the car-top control remains set to test

C) Turn off the shaft lights and switch the car-top control to normal

D) Press the stop button and switch the car-top control to normal

## 21.42

What precaution must you take if the landing doors are to be open while work goes on in the lift pit?

A) Erect a suitable barrier and secure it in front of the landing doors

B) Post a notice on the wall next to the doors

C) Do the job when there are few people about

D) Ask someone to guard the open doors while you work

## 21.43

What is the **first** thing to do after opening the landing doors and before accessing the car-top of an operating lift?

A) Chock the landing doors open

B) Press the car-top stop button

C) Make sure the lift has stopped

D) Put the car-top control in the test position

## 21.44

When you gain access to a car top, how should you test that the car-top stop switch operates correctly?

A) By trying to move the car in the up direction

B) By trying to move the car in the down direction

C) By measuring with a multimeter

D) By flicking the switch on and off rapidly

## 21.45

When working in the pit, when should the lift **not** be positioned towards the top of the shaft?

A) When the hydraulic fluid level is low

B) When the power supply is cut

C) When you are testing the buffers

D) When work needs to be done on the underside of the lift

## 21.46

What is required on each landing of a new lift shaft before entrances and doors are fitted?

A) A warning notice

B) A substantial secure barrier to prevent falls

C) Orange plastic netting across the opening

D) Bright lighting

**F**
21

Answers: 21.41 = B   21.42 = A   21.43 = C   21.44 = B   21.45 = D   21.46 = B

## 21.47

When handling stainless steel car panels, which of the following items of personal protective equipment (PPE) should you wear in addition to safety footwear?

A Suitable safety gloves, such as rigger type gloves

B Hand barrier cream

C Latex gloves

D Hearing protection

## 21.48

At what stage in the installation of a lift should guarding be fitted to the lift machine?

A At the end of the job

B During commissioning

C When handing over to the client

D Before the machine can be operated

## 21.49

Which of these statements is **not** true?

A A stop switch must be within 1.5 m of the front of the car

B The car top should be clean and free from grease and oil spills

C You should secure your tools out of your standing area when working on top of the car

D Before trying to access the hoist way, you should decide whether the work will need the power supply to be live

## 21.50

If one person has to work above another in a lift shaft what can you do to reduce the risk of the person below being harmed by falling objects?

A Minimise the tools and equipment in use above

B Have tools on lanyards

C Use safety helmets

D All of these answers

F
21

Answers: 21.47 = A   21.48 = D   21.49 = A   21.50 = D

# 22 Tunnelling

## 22.1

When working underground where should your self-rescue set be?

- A) On your person
- B) Immediately available
- C) At the nearest fire point
- D) Within two minutes' walking distance

## 22.2

The duration of a self-rescue set would be significantly reduced if the wearer uses it while:

- A) running
- B) waiting for rescue
- C) standing still
- D) smoking

## 22.3

BS 6164 states a self-rescue set used for escape should have a supply of air lasting at least:

- A) 5 minutes
- B) 10 minutes
- C) 20 minutes
- D) 30 minutes

## 22.4

In the event of an emergency who will use the information displayed on a tally board?

- A) Health and Safety Executive (HSE)
- B) DSS
- C) Rescue services
- D) Environmental Health

## 22.5

In the event of discovering a fire whilst in a tunnel, you should:

- A) leave the tunnel immediately
- B) leave the tunnel immediately and then raise the alarm
- C) contact your supervisor and report the fire's location
- D) raise the alarm and leave the tunnel, if safe to do so

## 22.6

Entry and exit of all personnel with regard to a confined space should be controlled by:

- A) CCTV
- B) light signals
- C) a tally system
- D) verbal communication with the top man

**F**
22

Answers: 22.1 = B   22.2 = A   22.3 = C   22.4 = C   22.5 = D   22.6 = C

## 22.7

Which of the following is **not** permitted underground?

A) The use of diesel

B) Smoking or smoking materials

C) Welding equipment

D) Gas bottles

## 22.8

What action should you take if the ventilation system alarm activates?

A) Carry on working until advised otherwise

B) Stop work and take a break

C) Evacuate the workplace

D) Ask your workmates

## 22.9

The atmosphere is oxygen deficient when the level of oxygen falls below:

A) 18%

B) 19%

C) 20%

D) 21%

## 22.10

Petrol-operated equipment:

A) is not allowed underground

B) can only be used for underground lighting

C) is used for all power sources

D) can be used with an exhaust filter

## 22.11

Intrinsically safe equipment should be used in the underground environment where there is a risk of encountering:

A) water

B) potentially explosive atmosphere

C) air

D) poisonous gas

## 22.12

All diesel engine plant used underground should be fitted with a:

A) toilet

B) fire detection system

C) fixed extinguishing system

D) portable extinguishing system

## 22.13

An oxygen-deficient atmosphere will leave you:

A) feeling happy

B) breathless

C) acting drunk

D) feeling excited

## 22.14

Underground petrol-operated equipment is:

A) used intermittently to prevent a build-up of fumes

B) the only equipment to be used

C) not to be used at all

D) used only if fitted with exhaust filters

**F**
**22**

Answers: 22.7 = B   22.8 = C   22.9 = B   22.10 = A   22.11 = B   22.12 = C
22.13 = B   22.14 = C

## 22.15

Methane gas does **not** have an odour. In what **two** ways can it be dangerous?

A  It causes skin irritation

B  It can cause temporary blindness

C  It is explosive

D  It is toxic

E  It reduces oxygen in the atmosphere

## 22.16

Which of the following is one way to tell that there may be hydrogen sulphide in the air?

A  There is a smell of rotten eggs

B  There is a yellow dust

C  A mist forms

D  You feel excited

## 22.17

Which of the following is a reliable way to detect carbon monoxide and methane gas?

A  They both have a distinctive bad egg smell

B  They are both harmless

C  With a calibrated gas detector

D  They both form a mist

## 22.18

How could hydrogen sulphide affect those working in a tunnel?

A  It can leave a yellow dust which can irritate the skin

B  It can make the atmosphere explosive

C  It can cause a mist making it difficult to see

D  It can cause death through stopping breathing

## 22.19

Carbon monoxide is dangerous because it:

A  is soluble in water

B  is a skin irritant

C  is an explosive

D  stops the intake of oxygen

## 22.20

What should indicate that the ventilation system has stopped working?

A  A notice at the daily briefing

B  You are informed as part of your induction

C  An audible alarm sounds

D  Your supervisor would inform you

F
22

## 22.21

Nitrogen oxide (NO) gas can be present in tunnels. Which one of these plant items causes most nitrogen oxide to be generated or made?

A. Tunnel-boring machines (TBMs)

B. Electro-hydraulic spray pumps

C. Rail-mounted plant

D. Diesel-powered equipment

## 22.22

Exposure to nitrogen oxide (NO) gas can cause breathing problems. Which of the following is the **preferred** control measure?

A. Provide air monitoring

B. Have a portable breathing set nearby

C. Avoid exposure

D. Provide ventilation systems

## 22.23

The power supply for communication equipment should be:

A. linked to the main tunnel power supply

B. independent of the main tunnel power supply

C. linked to the 33 kVA power supply

D. battery-powered

## 22.24

What is a common method used for communication between the tunnelling face and the surface?

A. Email

B. A two-way radio or tannoy system

C. Mobile phones

D. Text messages

## 22.25

The distance between emergency lighting in a tunnel should **not** exceed:

A. 25 m

B. 50 m

C. 75 m

D. 100 m

## 22.26

Mains-powered, electrically operated, portable hand tools **must** be:

A. 42 volts

B. 110 volts

C. 240 volts

D. 415 volts

## 22.27

What is the colour of a 415 volt plug?

A. Black

B. Blue

C. Yellow

D. Red

**F**
22

Answers: 22.21 = D   22.22 = C   22.23 = B   22.24 = B   22.25 = B   22.26 = B
22.27 = D

## 22.28

When working in a tunnel:

A  smoking can take place in all underground tunnels

B  smoking materials can be taken underground

C  smoking materials are not permitted underground

D  only cigarette smoking is permitted

## 22.29

Why is smoking **not** allowed underground?

A  Smoking is damaging to health

B  Smoking is a fire hazard

C  Non-smoking workers have complained

D  You can't smoke while wearing personal protective equipment (PPE)

## 22.30

When charging lead acid batteries they produce an explosive gas, smoking or other naked flames are **not** permitted within what distance of a battery-charging area?

A  5 m

B  10 m

C  15 m

D  20 m

## 22.31

Hot work activities are **not** permitted within what distance of a diesel-fuelling point?

A  5 m

B  10 m

C  15 m

D  20 m

## 22.32

As a minimum, how long **must** a fire watch be maintained after hot works have been completed?

A  15 minutes

B  30 minutes

C  45 minutes

D  60 minutes

## 22.33

The British Standard for tunnelling states that:

A  smoking materials should be prohibited underground

B  smoking is allowed anywhere below ground

C  designated smoking areas should be set up below ground

D  patches and gum should be provided for smokers working in tunnels

F
22

### 22.34

In compressed air tunnelling the term DCI refers to:

A dizzy, confused, induced state

B decompression incident

C decompression, combustion incident

D decompression illness

### 22.35

Which of the following characteristics are associated with hydrogen sulphide gas?

A A smell of rotten eggs

B It causes skin irritation

C It is odourless

D It causes a yellow haze

### 22.36

Which of the following statements is correct regarding hand-arm vibration syndrome?

A It can be prevented if gloves are worn

B It can be partially cured with medication

C It can be corrected by surgery

D Once damage has happened it cannot be cured

### 22.37

Batching plants **must** be equipped with:

A spanners for required repairs

B sterile bandages

C a first aider

D an eyewash station

### 22.38

What main health risk is **not** usually associated with using sprayed concrete linings?

A Cement burns

B Arc eye

C Hand-arm vibration syndrome

D Inhalation of dust

### 22.39

What is the biggest risk to health associated with hydrogen sulphide gas?

A It can irritate the eyes and throat

B It causes skin irritation

C It causes hand-arm vibration syndrome

D It causes respiratory paralysis

### 22.40

Which of the following is **not** a hazard associated with hand mining?

A Vibrating hand tools

B Noise

C Falling mined material

D Sprayed concrete rebound

F
22

Answers: 22.34 = D   22.35 = A   22.36 = D   22.37 = D   22.38 = B   22.39 = D
22.40 = D

## 22.41

When should a hop up or refuge in the tunnel be used?

A When vehicles are passing

B For services such as cables

C When installing ventilation cassettes

D For storage of materials and equipment

## 22.42

Which of the following **must** be fitted as a conveyor system safety device?

A Emergency lighting

B Emergency pull cord or stop button

C Hazard lighting

D Seat

## 22.43

Secondary couplings **must** be fitted to unbraked rolling stock to reduce the risk of it:

A being derailed

B running away

C being overloaded

D stalling

## 22.44

A locomotive or vehicle is approaching you in the tunnel. When should you make your way to a hop up/safe refuge?

A Immediately

B Only when you can see it

C When you have identified the direction of travel

D Only when everyone else starts to move

## 22.45

Audible alarms are fitted to conveyors to warn those nearby that:

A it is about to stop

B it is about to break down

C it is about to start

D the belt needs replacing

## 22.46

A locomotive is entering the rear of the tunnel-boring machine. Which **two** electronic systems are recommended to assist in controlling its movements?

A Signal or traffic lights

B CCTV in the cab

C Siren

D Telephone

E Klaxon bell

F
22

## 22.47

Inclined conveyors are fitted with anti-roll back devices to prevent the belt running backwards due to which **two** potential failures?

A Overloading

B Power loss

C Oil spillage

D Overheating

E Water leak

## 22.48

A common traffic light system used underground to control plant movement is:

A red = stop
amber = out bye
green = in bye

B red = stop
amber = in bye
green = out bye

C red = in bye
amber = stop
green = out bye

D red = out bye
amber = in bye
green = stop

## 22.49

The lights fitted on locomotives **must** be visible at a minimum distance of:

A 50 m

B 60 m

C 70 m

D 80 m

## 22.50

Alarms are fitted to a tunnel-boring machine's rams and erectors to warn workers when they:

A are moving or about to move

B are being maintained

C have completed the tunnel bore

D are stopping

## 22.51

A locomotive is travelling in the tunnel and you see a red light. This indicates that the locomotive:

A has stopped

B is travelling towards you

C is travelling away from you

D has broken down

## 22.52

What is the likely hazard from moving plant or locomotives in a tunnel?

A Crush

B Crash

C Noise

D Asphyxiation

## 22.53

Identify the **least** effective method of controlling locomotive movements in the pit bottom.

A Traffic lights

B Radio

C Shouting

D Hand signals

F
22

Answers: 22.47 = A, B   22.48 = A   22.49 = B   22.50 = A   22.51 = C   22.52 = A
22.53 = C

## 22.54

In an emergency a locomotive **must** be able to stop within a distance **not** exceeding:

- A) 600 m
- B) 100 m
- C) 60 m
- D) 10 m

## 22.55

How often should safe-refuge (hop ups) be located along a tunnel?

- A) 50 m on straights;
  25 m on curves
- B) 60 m on straights;
  30 m on curves
- C) 70 m on straights;
  25 m on curves
- D) 80 m on straights;
  20 m on curves

## 22.56

The tunnel-boring machine operator has restricted vision during the building process. Which of the following is the most effective way of overcoming this?

- A) Alternative control point
- B) Mirrors at shoulder or crane level
- C) Use a signaller
- D) Get one of the gang to build

## 22.57

A locomotive is travelling in the tunnel and you see a white light. This means that the locomotive:

- A) has stopped
- B) is travelling towards you
- C) is travelling away from you
- D) has broken down

## 22.58

Identify a potential for accidents arising from pumped grouting operations.

- A) Injury through a hose bursting
- B) Potential hearing loss due to noise
- C) Injury through blowout at the injection point
- D) All of these answers

## 22.59

Blockages in grouting pipelines can cause the pipe to burst. What is the **first** action to be taken?

- A) Locate the blockage
- B) Split the line
- C) Clean out section by section
- D) Release the pressure in the pipeline

F
22

Answers: 22.54 = C   22.55 = A   22.56 = A   22.57 = B   22.58 = D   22.59 = D

## 22.60

Why is it important to clean grouting pipelines after use to prevent injury to workers?

- A  It helps prevent blockages, which could cause the hose to burst
- B  It helps prevent the pipes from becoming weakened
- C  It keeps the dust level below the point that dust masks are needed
- D  It prevents the atmosphere from becoming explosive

## 22.61

Damaged flexible hoses can cause injury. One visible sign that a hose may be damaged is:

- A  swelling of the connections
- B  swelling of the hose
- C  difficulty in making a connection
- D  hardening of the rubber

## 22.62

Anti-whip devices **must** be fitted across:

- A  flexible hose connections
- B  rail connections
- C  steel pipe connections
- D  locomotive couplings

## 22.63

Anti-whip devices fitted to flexible hoses are designed to prevent:

- A  sudden parting of the connection under pressure
- B  a build up of dust
- C  hose ends flying about if they suddenly disconnect under pressure
- D  whole body vibration

## 22.64

To prevent injury during maintenance work on slurry lines a safe system of work should include which of the following?

- A  Isolation arrangements
- B  Report to the CDM co-ordinator
- C  Radar detection
- D  Unauthorised use

## 22.65

Which of the following statements is **not** true with regard to two hoses with different markings?

- A  They are different sizes
- B  They have different operating capacities
- C  They have different applications
- D  They can safely be joined together

## 22.66

Crash cages and side bars or sliding doors should be fitted to all man-riding cars used in the tunnel. Select **two** reasons why they are needed.

A To prevent derailment of the man-riding car

B To minimise injury in the event of a derailment

C To allow personnel to talk while being transported

D To stop personnel sitting close together

E To prevent personnel leaning out or falling out

## 22.67

Entry and exit to any tunnel under construction should be controlled by:

A CCTV

B a tally system

C verbal communication

D control is not necessary

## 22.68

For maintenance purposes water in the tunnel should **not** be allowed to accumulate at or above:

A axis level

B rail level

C walkway level

D crown level

## 22.69

Vertical ladders in shafts **must** have a landing interval every:

A 4 m

B 6 m

C 8 m

D 10 m

## 22.70

For tunnelling operations what is the minimum number of escape routes or methods that **must** be maintained from a working shaft?

A One

B Two

C Three

D Four

## 22.71

What term is used for the access and egress control system to tunnels?

A Visitor book

B Tally system

C Signing-in book

D Control is not needed

F
22

## 22.72

If a man-riding cage is used to transport workers into and out of a shaft, how many people can be transported at any one time?

A As defined by the Health and Safety Executive (HSE)

B As many as can fit into it

C As many as stated on the man-rider

D As many as stated by the supervisor

## 22.73

In straight sections of tunnel what is the recommended maximum distance between safe refuges?

A 25 m

B 50 m

C 75 m

D They are not required

## 22.74

On curved sections of tunnel what is the recommended maximum distance between safe refuges?

A Any distance

B 15 m

C 25 m

D 35 m

## 22.75

Compressed air tunnelling is used to:

A prevent water from leaving the tunnel

B avoid gas build up in the tunnel

C stop air escaping from the tunnel

D prevent and/or reduce water ingress during tunnel construction

## 22.76

Tunnel services should be correctly located to ensure:

A they cannot be seen

B they are in a safe position

C they are in an unsafe position

D it doesn't matter as any position works

## 22.77

Hydraulic jacking rams in a pipe-jacking shaft or pit should be fitted with:

A cushions to sit on

B audible or visual alarm to alert when moving

C the manufacturer's label

D a two-way radio

## 22.78

BS 6164 is the code of practice for safety in:

A construction

B tunnelling

C land management

D construction, design and management

F
22

Answers: 22.72 = C   22.73 = B   22.74 = C   22.75 = D   22.76 = B   22.77 = B
22.78 = B

### 22.79

Underground, a water spray curtain can help in slowing down the movement of:

A smoke

B unpleasant smells

C vermin

D waste skips

### 22.80

Segment erector equipment should have a fail to safety device to stop the operation in case of:

A malfunction, leakage or power failure

B electrocution

C anti-clockwise rotation

D overloading

### 22.81

A safe system of work for track maintenance **must** include which **two** of the following?

A A permit to work

B Red and green flags

C Adequate refuge space

D Crash deflectors

E A report for the CDM co-ordinator

### 22.82

A secure barrier **must** be maintained around any shaft to prevent falls. What is the minimum recommended height of the barrier?

A 0.9 m

B 1.2 m

C 1.5 m

D 1.8 m

### 22.83

What other controls should be used to warn locomotive drivers of personnel working in the tunnel?

A Permit system

B Trackside warning lights

C Lookouts and workers wearing hi-vis clothes

D All of these answers

### 22.84

Where a hazard cannot be eliminated the next control measure is for the risks to be:

A minimised

B disabled

C monitored

D accepted

F
22

## 22.85

Which of the following controls should be considered for shafts under construction?

A) Ventilation

B) Continuous gas monitoring

C) Shaft guarding

D) All of these answers

## 22.86

Stored tunnel segments should be secured by suitable means to prevent:

A) damage to the segments

B) additional loading on tunnel excavations

C) segments toppling over

D) all of these answers

## 22.87

Workers should **not** be allowed to work alone in tunnels because:

A) nobody will know whether they have had an accident and they may be unable to communicate

B) they may get lonely

C) the CDM co-ordinator has prevented it

D) they may lose track of time

## 22.88

Which of the following situations would require using a safety harness?

A) Working as the signaller at the pit top

B) Working as the belt-man on a TBM

C) Landing concrete jacking-pipes in the pit bottom

D) Building rings from a platform within a shaft

## 22.89

Oxygen cylinders should **not** be allowed to come into contact with which of the following substances?

A) Mud

B) Grease

C) Paint

D) Air

## 22.90

While walking through the tunnel you see a tear in the ventilation ducting. What should you do?

A) Report it to your supervisor

B) Try to repair it

C) Check if it has got any bigger at the end of the shift

D) Evacuate the tunnel

**F 22**

Answers: 22.85 = D   22.86 = D   22.87 = A   22.88 = D   22.89 = B   22.90 = A

## 22.91

If a blockage occurs during sprayed concrete operations the **first** action to be taken is to:

- A) release pressure in the line
- B) uncouple jointed pipes
- C) increase pressure in the line
- D) hit the line with a lump hammer

## 22.92

The most significant hazard from freshly applied sprayed concrete lining is:

- A) material rebounding off the tunnel wall
- B) material falling to crush workers
- C) not wearing the right personal protective equipment (PPE)
- D) workers being trapped by the equipment

## 22.93

One of the main hazards during shaft sinking operations is:

- A) suspended loads
- B) caulking
- C) locomotive movements
- D) maintenance work

## 22.94

The biggest risk from suspended loads during shaft sinking operations is:

- A) damage to the shaft walls
- B) falling objects and failure of the suspended load
- C) restriction on the lifting capacity
- D) restricted vision of the crane driver

## 22.95

When uncoupling or disconnecting hoses or pipework, operatives should firstly:

- A) isolate and release any stored energy or pressure
- B) check fluid levels
- C) part uncouple or disconnect and check for leaks
- D) ensure that any stored energy is not released

## 22.96

What hazards need to be controlled during sprayed concrete operations?

- A) Manual handling activities
- B) Rebound of materials
- C) Slips, trips and falls
- D) All of these answers

F
22

## 22.97

Guards on grout mixers help prevent injury to operators. Before removing a guard you **must** ensure that the:

A) Health and Safety Executive (HSE) has been notified

B) power has been isolated

C) hose whip restraints are in place

D) CDM co-ordinator has been notified

## 22.98

A grout gun inserted into a segment grout hole may present which of the following hazards?

A) Shrinking grout hose

B) Falls from height

C) Blowout at injection point

D) Hand-arm vibration

## 22.99

Which of the following personal protective equipment (PPE) is **not** normally required for robotic-sprayed concrete lining operations in tunnelling?

A) Eye protection

B) Respiratory protective equipment

C) Disposable overalls

D) Safety harness

F
22

# 23 HVACR – HAPS Heating and plumbing services

## 23.1

You have to drill through a wall panel that you suspect contains an asbestos material. What should you do?

[A] Use a low speed drill setting

[B] Spray it with water as you drill

[C] Put on an FFP3-rated dust mask before drilling

[D] Stop work and report it

## 23.2

When a new piece of plant has been installed but has **not** been commissioned, how should it be left?

[A] With all valves and switches turned off

[B] With all valves and switches clearly labelled

[C] With all valves and switches locked off

[D] With all valves and switches turned on and ready to use

## 23.3

Who can change a gas valve on a gas boiler?

[A] A skilled engineer

[B] A pipefitter

[C] A Gas Safe registered engineer

[D] Anybody

## 23.4

Who can solder a fitting on an isolated copper gas pipe?

[A] A plumber

[B] A pipefitter

[C] A skilled welder

[D] A Gas Safe registered engineer

## 23.5

When working in a riser, how should access be controlled?

[A] By a site security operative

[B] By those who are working in it

[C] By the main contractor

[D] By a permit to work system

## 23.6

If you find a coloured wire sticking out of an electrical plug what is the correct action to take?

[A] Push it back into the plug and carry on working

[B] Pull the wire clear of the plug and report it to your supervisor

[C] Mark the item as defective and follow your company procedure for defective items

[D] Take the plug apart and carry out a repair

**F 23**

Answers: 23.1 = D   23.2 = C   23.3 = C   23.4 = D   23.5 = D   23.6 = C

## 23.7

How should extension leads in use on site be positioned?

A) They should be located so as to prevent a tripping hazard

B) They should be laid out in the shortest, most convenient route

C) They should be coiled on a drum or cable tidy

D) They should be raised on bricks

## 23.8

What should you do if you need additional temporary wiring for your power tools whilst working on site?

A) Find some cable and extend the wiring yourself

B) Stop work until an authorised supply has been installed

C) Speak to an electrician and ask them to do the temporary wiring

D) Disconnect a longer cable serving somewhere else and reconnect it to where you need it

## 23.9

Which of the following electrical equipment does **not** require portable appliance testing?

A) Battery-powered rechargeable drill

B) 110 volt electrical drill

C) 110 volt portable halogen light

D) Electric kettle

## 23.10

Why is temporary continuity bonding carried out before removing and replacing sections of metallic pipework?

A) To provide a continuous earth for the pipework installation

B) To prevent any chance of blowing a fuse

C) To maintain the live supply to the electrical circuit

D) To prevent any chance of corrosion to the pipework

## 23.11

Which type of power drill is most suitable for fixing a run of pipework outside in wet weather?

A) Battery-powered drill

B) Drill with 110 volt power supply

C) Drill with 240 volt power supply

D) Any mains voltage drill with a power breaker

## 23.12

What would you use to find out whether a wall into which you are about to drill contains an electric supply?

A) A neon screwdriver

B) A cable tracer

C) A multimeter

D) A hammer and chisel

**F**
23

## 23.13

Where should liquefied petroleum gas (LPG) cylinders be positioned when supplying an appliance in a site cabin?

- A Inside the cabin in a locked cupboard
- B Under the cabin
- C Inside the cabin next to the appliance
- D Outside the cabin

## 23.14

How should you position the exhaust of an engine-driven generator that has to be run inside a building?

- A Outside the building
- B In a stairwell
- C In another room
- D In a riser

## 23.15

How should cylinders containing liquefied petroleum gas (LPG) be stored on site?

- A In a locked cellar with clear warning signs
- B In a locked cage at least 3 m from any oxygen cylinders
- C Within a secure storage container at the back of the site
- D Covered by a tarpaulin to shield the compressed cylinder from sunlight

## 23.16

You spill some oil on the floor and you do **not** have any absorbent material to clean the area. What should you do?

- A Spread it about to lessen the depth
- B Keep people out of the area and inform your supervisor
- C Do nothing, it will eventually soak into the floor
- D Warn other people as they tread through it

## 23.17

If you find a dangerous gas fitting that is likely to cause a death or specified injury, who **must** be sent a formal report?

- A The client
- B The gas board
- C The health and safety manager
- D The Health and Safety Executive (HSE)

## 23.18

What is the colour of propane gas cylinders?

- A Black
- B Maroon
- C Red or orange
- D Blue

F
23

Answers: 23.13 = D    23.14 = A    23.15 = B    23.16 = B    23.17 = D    23.18 = C

## 23.19

When **must** you wear eye protection while drilling through a wall?

A Only when drilling overhead

B Only when the drill bit exceeds 20 mm

C Always, whatever the circumstances

D Only when drilling through concrete

## 23.20

What personal protective equipment (PPE) should you wear when using a hammer drill to drill a 100 mm diameter hole through a brick wall?

A Gloves, breathing apparatus and boots

B Ear defenders, face mask, boots and eye protection

C Ear defenders, breathing apparatus and barrier cream

D Barrier cream, boots and face mask

## 23.21

What should you do when using pipe-freezing equipment to isolate a damaged section of pipe?

A Always work in pairs when using pipe-freezing equipment

B Never allow the freezing gas to come into direct contact with surface water

C Never use pipe-freezing equipment on plastic pipe

D Wear gloves to avoid direct contact with the skin and read the COSHH assessment

## 23.22

If you are working where welding is being carried out, what should be provided to protect you from welding flash?

A Fire extinguishers

B Warning notices

C Screens

D Hi-vis vest

## 23.23

When using a blowtorch to joint copper tube and fittings in a domestic property, how should a fire extinguisher be made available?

A It should be available in the immediate work area

B It should be held over the joint while you are using the blowtorch

C It should be kept away from the work area in case a spark causes it to explode

D It should be available only if a property is occupied

## 23.24

When using a blowtorch, when should you stop working with the blowtorch before leaving the job?

A Immediately before leaving the work

B At least one hour after finishing the work

C At least two hours after finishing the work

D At least four hours after finishing the work

**F**
**23**

## 23.25

What should you do when using a blowtorch near to flexible pipe lagging?

- A Wet the lagging but leave it in place
- B Remove just enough lagging to carry out the job
- C Remove the lagging at least 3 m either side of the work
- D Remove the lagging at least 1 m either side of the work

## 23.26

What should you do when using a blowtorch near to timber?

- A Carry out the work, taking care not to set fire to the timber
- B Wet the timber first and have a bucket of water handy
- C Use a non-combustible mat and have a fire extinguisher in the immediate work area
- D Point the flame away from the timber and have a bucket of sand ready to put out the fire

## 23.27

The legionella bacteria that cause legionnaires' disease are most likely to be found in which of the following?

- A A boiler operating at a temperature of 80°C
- B An infrequently used shower hose outlet
- C A cold water storage cistern containing water at 10°C
- D A toilet pan

## 23.28

How are legionella bacteria passed on to humans?

- A Through fine water droplets, such as sprays or mists
- B By drinking dirty water
- C Through contact with the skin
- D From other people when they sneeze

## 23.29

When planning a lifting operation, how should the sequence of operations to enable a safe lift be confirmed?

- A Using verbal instruction
- B In a method statement
- C In a radio telephone message
- D On a notice in the canteen

## 23.30

Which **one** of these is true in relation to the safe working load (SWL) of lifting equipment?

- A It is never marked on the equipment but kept with the test certificates
- B It is provided for guidance only
- C It may be exceeded by no more than 25%
- D It is the maximum safe working load

F
23

## 23.31

What **must** be clearly marked on all lifting equipment?

A. The name of the manufacturer

B. The safe working load

C. The next test date

D. The specification of material from which it's made

## 23.32

You are required to take up a length of floorboard to install pipework. Which of the following tools should you use?

A. A hammer and wood chisel

B. A hammer and screwdriver

C. A hammer and bolster

D. A chainsaw

## 23.33

What is the safest method of taking long lengths of copper pipe by van?

A. Tying the pipes to the roof with copper wire

B. Someone holding the pipes on the roof rack as you drive along

C. Putting the pipes inside the van with the ends out of the passenger window

D. Using a pipe rack fixed to the roof of the van

## 23.34

You are asked to move a cast-iron boiler some distance. What is the safest method?

A. Get a workmate to carry it with you

B. Drag it

C. Roll it end-over-end

D. Use a trolley or other manual handling aid

## 23.35

During a job you may need to work below a ground-level suspended timber floor. What is the **first** question you should ask?

A. Can the work be performed from outside?

B. Will temporary lighting be used?

C. What is contained under the floor?

D. How many ways in or out are there?

## 23.36

When carrying a ladder on a vehicle, what is the correct way of securing the ladder to the roof rack?

A. Rope

B. Bungee elastics

C. Ladder clamps

D. Copper wire

F
23

Answers: 23.31 = B   23.32 = C   23.33 = D   23.34 = D   23.35 = A   23.36 = C

## 23.37

What **must** you ensure before using a ladder?

A. That it is secured to prevent it from moving sideways or sliding outwards

B. That no-one else has booked the ladder for their work

C. That an apprentice or workmate is standing by in case you slip and fall

D. That the weather forecast is for a bright, clear day

## 23.38

When positioning and erecting a stepladder, which of the following is essential for its safe use?

A. It has a tool tray towards the top of the steps

B. The restraint mechanism is spread to its full extent

C. You will be able to reach the job by standing on the top step

D. A competent person has positioned and erected the steps

## 23.39

What is the recommended maximum height for a free-standing mobile tower?

A. There is no recommended height

B. 2 m

C. The height recommended by the manufacturer

D. 12 m

## 23.40

What is the **first** thing you should do after getting on to the platform of a mobile tower?

A. Check that the brakes are locked on

B. Check the mobile tower to make sure that it has been correctly assembled

C. Close the access hatch to prevent falls of personnel, tools or equipment

D. Make sure that the tower does not rock or wobble

## 23.41

What should be done before a mobile tower is moved?

A. All people and equipment must be removed from the platform

B. A permit to work must be issued

C. The principal contractor must give their approval

D. Arrangements must be made with the forklift truck driver

## 23.42

What must be done **first** before any roof work is carried out?

A. A risk assessment must be carried out

B. The operatives working on the roof must be trained in the use of safety harnesses

C. Permits to work must be issued only to those allowed to work on the roof

D. A weather forecast must be obtained

F
23

## 23.43

What is edge protection designed to do?

A. Make access to the roof easier

B. Secure tools and materials close to the edge

C. Prevent rainwater running off the roof onto workers below

D. Prevent the fall of people and materials

## 23.44

What is the **first** thing you should do after getting on to the platform of a correctly erected mobile tower?

A. Check that the brakes are locked on

B. Check the mobile tower to make sure that it has been correctly assembled

C. Close the access hatch to prevent falls of personnel, tools or equipment

D. Make sure that the tower does not rock or wobble

## 23.45

What major overhead hazard **must** you be aware of when assembling a mobile tower?

A. Water pipes

B. Cable trays

C. False ceilings

D. Overhead service cables

## 23.46

What should folding stepladders be used for?

A. General access on site

B. Short-term work

C. All site activities where a straight ladder cannot be used

D. Getting on and off mobile towers

## 23.47

When drilling a hole for a boiler flue outside, which type of working platform should you use?

A. A long ladder

B. Borrowed scaffolding that you have erected

C. A mobile tower or fixed scaffold

D. Packing cases to stand on

## 23.48

How should you access a roof to install a flexible flue liner into an existing chimney?

A. Work from a roof ladder securely hooked over the ridge

B. Use an access scaffold designed for chimney works

C. Scramble up the roof tiles to get to the chimney

D. Get your mate to do the job while you hold a rope tied to them

F
23

**23.49**

When is the **only** circumstance when stepladders should be used?

A   Inside buildings

B   If no other suitable equipment is available after works have been risk assessed

C   If they are made of aluminium

D   If they are less than 1.75 m high

F
23

## 24 HVACR – PFW Pipefitting and welding

### 24.1

When a new piece of plant has been installed but has **not** been commissioned, how should it be left?

A With all valves and switches turned off

B With all valves and switches clearly labelled

C With all valves and switches locked off

D With all valves and switches turned on and ready to use

### 24.2

Who is allowed to install natural gas pipework?

A A skilled engineer

B A pipefitter

C A Gas Safe registered engineer

D Anybody

### 24.3

Who should carry out pressure testing on pipework or vessels?

A Anyone who is available

B A competent person

C A Health and Safety Executive (HSE) inspector

D A building control officer

### 24.4

When working in a riser, how should access be controlled?

A By a site security operative

B By those who are working in it

C By the main contractor

D By a permit to work system

### 24.5

While working on your own and tracing pipework in a building, you notice that the pipes enter a service duct. What should you do?

A Go into the service duct and continue to trace the pipework

B Ask someone in the building to act as your second person

C Put on your personal protective equipment (PPE) and carry on with the job

D Stop work until a risk assessment has been carried out

### 24.6

If you find a coloured wire sticking out of an electrical plug what is the correct action to take?

A Push it back into the plug and carry on working

B Pull the wire clear of the plug and report it to your supervisor

C Mark the item as defective and follow your company procedure for defective items

D Take the plug apart and carry out a repair

F
24

Answers: 24.1 = C   24.2 = C   24.3 = B   24.4 = D   24.5 = D   24.6 = C

## 24.7

How should extension leads in use on site be positioned?

A They should be located so as to prevent a tripping hazard

B They should be laid out in the shortest, most convenient route

C They should be coiled on a drum or cable tidy

D They should be raised on bricks

## 24.8

What should you do if you need additional temporary wiring for your power tools whilst working on site?

A Find some cable and extend the wiring yourself

B Stop work until an authorised supply has been installed

C Speak to an electrician and ask them to do the temporary wiring

D Disconnect a longer cable serving somewhere else and reconnect it to where you need it

## 24.9

Which of the following electrical equipment does **not** require portable appliance testing?

A Battery-powered rechargeable drill

B 110 volt electrical drill

C 110 volt portable halogen light

D Electric kettle

## 24.10

Where should liquefied petroleum gas (LPG) cylinders be positioned when supplying an appliance in a site cabin?

A Inside the cabin in a locked cupboard

B Under the cabin

C Inside the cabin next to the appliance

D Outside the cabin

## 24.11

How should you position the exhaust of an engine-driven generator that has to be run inside a building?

A Outside the building

B In a stairwell

C In another room

D In a riser

## 24.12

How should cylinders containing liquefied petroleum gas (LPG) be stored on site?

A In a locked cellar with clear warning signs

B In a locked cage at least 3 m from any oxygen cylinders

C As close to the point of use as possible

D Covered by a tarpaulin to shield the compressed cylinder from sunlight

**F**
24

## 24.13

You spill some oil on the floor and you do **not** have any absorbent material to clean the area. What should you do?

A) Spread it about to lessen the depth

B) Keep people out of the area and inform your supervisor

C) Do nothing, as it will eventually soak into the floor

D) Warn other people as they tread through it

## 24.14

What guarding is required when a pipe threading machine is in use?

A) A length of red material hung from the exposed end of the pipe

B) A barrier at the exposed end of the pipe only

C) A barrier around the whole of the pipe length and machine

D) Warning notices in the work area

## 24.15

What should you do when using pipe-freezing equipment to isolate a damaged section of pipe?

A) Always work in pairs

B) Never allow the freezing gas to come into direct contact with surface water

C) Never use pipe-freezing equipment on plastic pipe

D) Wear gloves to avoid direct contact with the skin and read the COSHH assessment

## 24.16

Why is it important to know the difference between propane and butane equipment?

A) Propane equipment operates at higher pressure

B) Propane equipment operates at lower pressure

C) Propane equipment is cheaper

D) Propane equipment can be used with smaller, easy-to-handle cylinders

## 24.17

Which of the following statements is **true**?

A) Both propane and butane are heavier than air

B) Butane is heavier than air while propane is lighter than air

C) Propane is heavier than air while butane is lighter than air

D) Both propane and butane are lighter than air

F
24

## 24.18

Apart from the cylinders used in gas-powered forklift trucks, why should you never see liquefied petroleum gas (LPG) cylinders placed on their side during use?

- A   It would give a faulty reading on the contents gauge, resulting in flashback
- B   Air could be drawn into the cylinder, creating a dangerous mixture of gases
- C   The liquid gas would be at too low a level to allow the torch to burn correctly
- D   The liquid gas could be drawn from the cylinder, creating a safety hazard

## 24.19

What is the method of checking for leaks after connecting a liquefied petroleum gas (LPG) regulator to the bottle?

- A   Test with a lighted match
- B   Sniff the connections to detect the smell of gas
- C   Listen to hear for escaping gas
- D   Apply leak detection fluid to the connections

## 24.20

What is the most likely risk of injury when cutting a pipe with hand-operated pipe cutters?

- A   Your fingers may become trapped between the cutting wheel and the pipe
- B   The inside edge of the cut pipe becomes extremely sharp
- C   Continued use can cause muscle damage
- D   Pieces of sharp metal could fly off

## 24.21

Why is it essential to take great care when handling oxygen cylinders?

- A   They contain highly flammable compressed gas
- B   They contain highly flammable liquid gas
- C   They are filled to extremely high pressures
- D   They contain poisonous gas

## 24.22

When do you need to wear eye protection while drilling through a wall?

- A   Only when drilling overhead
- B   Only when the drill bit exceeds 20 mm
- C   Always, whatever the circumstances
- D   Only when drilling through concrete

F
24

## 24.23

If you are working where welding is being carried out, what should be provided to protect you from welding flash?

A) Fire extinguishers

B) Warning notices

C) Screens

D) Hi-vis vest

## 24.24

What is the main hazard associated with flame-cutting and welding?

A) Gas poisoning

B) Fire

C) Dropping a gas cylinder

D) Not having a hot work permit

## 24.25

When should you stop using a blowtorch?

A) Immediately after finishing the work

B) At least one hour after finishing the work

C) At least two hours after finishing the work

D) At least four hours after finishing the work

## 24.26

What should you do when using a blowtorch near to flexible pipe lagging?

A) Remove the lagging at least 1 m either side of the work

B) Remove just enough lagging to carry out the work

C) Remove the lagging at least 3 m either side of the work

D) Wet the lagging but leave it in place

## 24.27

When using a blowtorch near to timber, what should you do?

A) Carry out the work taking care not to catch the timber

B) Point the flame away from the timber and have a bucket of sand ready to put out the fire

C) Wet the timber first and keep a bucket of water handy

D) Use a non-combustible mat and have a fire extinguisher ready

## 24.28

What is the colour of an acetylene cylinder?

A) Orange

B) Black

C) Green

D) Maroon

F
24

## 24.29

What particular item of personal protective equipment (PPE) should you use when oxyacetylene brazing?

A Ear defenders

B Clear goggles

C Green-tinted goggles

D Dust mask

## 24.30

When using oxyacetylene brazing equipment, how should the bottles be positioned?

A Laid on their side and secured

B Stood upright and secured

C Stood upside down

D Angled at 45° and secured against falling

## 24.31

The use of oxyacetylene equipment is **not** recommended for which of the following jointing methods?

A Jointing copper pipe using hard soldering

B Jointing copper tube using capillary soldered fittings

C Jointing mild steel tube

D Jointing sheet lead

## 24.32

Where should acetylene gas-welding bottles be stored when they are **not** in use?

A Outside in a special storage compound

B In a special rack in a company van

C Inside a building in a locked cupboard

D With oxygen bottles

## 24.33

When planning a lifting operation, how should the sequence of operations to enable a safe lift be confirmed?

A Using verbal instruction

B In a method statement

C In a radio telephone message

D On a notice in the canteen

## 24.34

Which of these statements is true in relation to the SWL of lifting equipment?

A It is never marked on the equipment but kept with the test certificates

B It is provided for guidance only

C It may be exceeded by no more than 25%

D It is the absolute maximum safe working load

F
24

## 24.35

What **must** be clearly marked on all lifting equipment?

[A] The name of the manufacturer

[B] The safe working load

[C] The next test date

[D] The specification of material from which it's made

## 24.36

Which **two** of the following are essential safety checks to be carried out before using oxyacetylene equipment?

[A] That the cylinders are full

[B] That the cylinders, hoses and flashback arresters are in good condition

[C] That the trolley wheels are the right size

[D] That the area is well ventilated and clear of any obstructions

[E] That the cylinders are the right weight

## 24.37

Who should be present during the pressure testing of pipework or vessels?

[A] The architect

[B] The site foreman

[C] Only those involved in carrying out the test

[D] Anybody

## 24.38

What should you ensure when using an electrically powered threading machine?

[A] That the power supply is 24 volts

[B] That the power supply is 415 volts and the machine is fitted with a guard

[C] That your clothing cannot get caught on rotating parts of the machine

[D] That the machine is only used in your compound

## 24.39

What **must** you ensure before using a ladder?

[A] That it is secured to prevent it from moving sideways or sliding outwards

[B] That no-one else has booked the ladder for their work

[C] That an apprentice or workmate is standing by in case you slip and fall

[D] That the weather forecast is for a bright, clear day

F
24

## 24.40

When positioning and erecting a stepladder, which of the following is essential for its safe use?

A  It has a tool tray towards the top of the steps

B  The restraint mechanism is spread to its full extent

C  You will be able to reach the job by standing on the top step

D  A competent person has positioned and erected the steps

## 24.41

What is the recommended maximum height for a free-standing mobile tower?

A  There is no restriction

B  2 m

C  The height recommended by the manufacturer

D  12 m

## 24.42

What should be done before a mobile tower is moved?

A  All people and equipment must be removed from the platform

B  A permit to work must be issued

C  The principal contractor must give their approval

D  Arrangements must be made with the forklift truck driver

## 24.43

What must be done **first** before any roof work is carried out?

A  A risk assessment must be carried out

B  The operatives working on the roof must be trained in the use of safety harnesses

C  Permits to work must be issued only to those allowed to work on the roof

D  A weather forecast must be obtained

## 24.44

What is edge protection designed to do?

A  Make access to the roof easier

B  Secure tools and materials close to the edge

C  Prevent rainwater running off the roof onto workers below

D  Prevent the fall of people and materials

## 24.45

What is the **first** thing you should do after getting on to the platform of a correctly erected mobile tower?

A  Check that the brakes are locked on

B  Check the mobile tower to make sure that it has been correctly assembled

C  Close the access hatch to prevent falls of personnel, tools or equipment

D  Make sure that the tower does not rock or wobble

F
24

Answers: 24.40 = B   24.41 = C   24.42 = A   24.43 = A   24.44 = D   24.45 = C   **183**

## 24.46

When assembling a mobile tower what major overhead hazard **must** you be aware of?

(A) Water pipes

(B) Cable trays

(C) False ceilings

(D) Overhead service cables

## 24.47

What should folding stepladders be used for?

(A) General access on site

(B) Short-term work

(C) All site activities where a straight ladder cannot be used

(D) Getting on and off mobile towers

## 24.48

You are asked to install high-level ductwork from a platform that has no edge protection and is located above an open stairwell. What should you do?

(A) Get on with the job, but keep away from the edge of the platform

(B) Not start work until your work platform has been fitted with guard-rails and toe-boards

(C) Get on with the job, ensuring that a workmate stays close by

(D) Get on with the job, provided that if you fall the stairwell guard-rail will prevent you from falling further

**F**
24

## 25 HVACR – DUCT
## Ductwork

### 25.1

When a new piece of plant has been installed but has **not** been commissioned, how should it be left?

A) With all valves and switches turned off

B) With all valves and switches clearly labelled

C) With all valves and switches locked off

D) With all valves and switches turned on and ready to use

### 25.2

Who should carry out leakage testing of a newly installed ductwork system?

A) The installation contractor

B) The property owner

C) The designer

D) A trained and competent person

### 25.3

When working in a riser, how should access be controlled?

A) By a site security operative

B) By those who are working in it

C) By the main contractor

D) By a permit to work system

### 25.4

If you find a coloured wire sticking out of an electrical plug what is the correct action to take?

A) Push it back into the plug and carry on working

B) Pull the wire clear of the plug and report it to your supervisor

C) Mark the item as defective and follow your company procedure for defective items

D) Take the plug apart and carry out a repair

### 25.5

How should extension leads in use on site be positioned?

A) They should be located so as to prevent a tripping hazard

B) They should be laid out in the shortest, most convenient route

C) They should be coiled on a drum or cable tidy

D) They should be raised on bricks

### 25.6

What should you do if you need additional temporary wiring for your power tools whilst working on site?

A) Find some cable and extend the wiring yourself

B) Stop work until an authorised supply has been installed

C) Speak to an electrician and ask them to do the temporary wiring

D) Disconnect a longer cable serving somewhere else and reconnect it to where you need it

F
25

Answers: 25.1 = C   25.2 = D   25.3 = D   25.4 = C   25.5 = A   25.6 = B

## 25.7

Which of the following electrical equipment does **not** require portable appliance testing?

A) Battery-powered rechargeable drill

B) 110 volt electrical drill

C) 110 volt portable halogen light

D) Electric kettle

## 25.8

Where should liquefied petroleum gas (LPG) cylinders be positioned when supplying an appliance in a site cabin?

A) Inside the cabin in a locked cupboard

B) Under the cabin

C) Inside the cabin next to the appliance

D) Outside the cabin

## 25.9

How should you position the exhaust of an engine-driven generator that has to be run inside a building?

A) Outside the building

B) In a stairwell

C) Hung in another room

D) In a riser

## 25.10

You spill some oil on the floor and you do **not** have any absorbent material to clean the area. What should you do?

A) Spread it about to lessen the depth

B) Keep people out of the area and inform your supervisor

C) Do nothing, it will eventually soak into the floor

D) Warn other people as they tread through it

## 25.11

What should you do if you see the side of an abrasive disc on a disc cutter being used to grind down the ends of a drop rod?

A) Check that the correct type of disc is being used

B) Stop the person immediately

C) Go and find your supervisor and report it

D) Check that the disc has not been subjected to over-speeding

## 25.12

Which **two** of the following should you use when cutting back sheet metal ductwork?

A) A hacksaw

B) Respiratory protection

C) A disc cutter

D) A set of tin snips

E) Ear defenders

F
25

## 25.13

A person who has been using a solvent-based ductwork sealant is complaining of headaches and feeling sick. What is the **first** thing you should do?

A) Let them carry on working but try to keep a close watch on them

B) Get them a drink of water and a headache tablet

C) Get them out to fresh air and make them rest

D) Stop work and tell your supervisor

## 25.14

What additional control measure must be put in place when welding in-situ galvanised ductwork?

A) Screens

B) Fume extraction

C) Warning signs

D) Hearing protection

## 25.15

When jointing plastic-coated metal ductwork, which of the following methods of jointing presents the most serious risk to health?

A) Welding

B) Taping

C) Riveting

D) Fixing nuts and bolts

## 25.16

You are removing a run of ductwork in an unoccupied building and notice a hypodermic syringe behind it. What should you do?

A) Ensure the syringe is empty, remove it and place it with the rubbish

B) Wear gloves, break the syringe into small pieces and flush it down the drain

C) Notify the supervisor, cordon off the area and call the emergency services

D) Wear gloves, use grips to remove the syringe to a safe place and report your find

## 25.17

If you are working where welding is being carried out, what should be provided to protect you from welding flash?

A) Fire extinguishers

B) Warning notices

C) Screens

D) Hi-vis vest

## 25.18

When planning a lifting operation, how should the sequence of operations to enable a safe lift be confirmed?

A) By verbal instructions

B) In a method statement

C) In a radio telephone message

D) Via a notice in the canteen

F
25

## 25.19

Which of these statements is true in relation to the SWL of lifting equipment?

A  It is never marked on the equipment but kept with the test certificates

B  It is provided for guidance only

C  It may be exceeded by no more than 25%

D  It is the absolute maximum safe working load

## 25.20

What **must** be clearly marked on all lifting equipment?

A  The name of the manufacturer

B  The safe working load

C  The next test date

D  The specification of material from which it's made

## 25.21

When using a material hoist you notice that the lifting cable is frayed. What should you do?

A  Get the job done as quickly as possible

B  Straighten out the cable using mole grips

C  Do not use the hoist and report the problem

D  Be very careful when using the hoist

## 25.22

When do you need to wear eye protection while drilling through a wall?

A  Only when drilling overhead

B  Only when the drill bit exceeds 20 mm

C  Always, whatever the circumstances

D  Only when drilling through concrete

## 25.23

In addition to a safety helmet and protective footwear, what personal protective equipment (PPE) should you wear when using a hammer drill?

A  Gloves and breathing apparatus

B  Hearing protection, face mask and eye protection

C  Hearing protection, breathing apparatus and barrier cream

D  Barrier cream and face mask

## 25.24

How should you leave the area around ductwork after using a solvent-based sealant?

A  Seal up all the open ends to ensure that dirt cannot get into the system

B  Ensure that the lids are left off tins of solvent

C  Remove any safety signs or notices

D  Leave inspection covers off and erect no smoking signs

F
25

## 25.25

Before taking down a run of ductwork, what is the **first** thing you should do?

(A) Assess the volume of waste and get an appropriate sized skip

(B) Cut through the support rods

(C) Clean the ductwork to remove all dust

(D) Assess the task to be undertaken and check its support system

## 25.26

You are asked to move a fan-coil unit some distance. What is the safest way to do it?

(A) Get a workmate to carry it with you

(B) Drag it

(C) Roll it end-over-end

(D) Use a trolley or other manual handling aid

## 25.27

While fitting a fire damper into a ductwork system you notice that, due to a manufacturing fault, it may **not** operate properly. What should you do?

(A) Install it anyway, as it is

(B) Fix it so that it stays open, and then install it

(C) Not fit the damper and report the fault

(D) Leave it out of the ductwork system altogether

## 25.28

You have to dismantle some waste-extract ductwork. What is the **first** thing you should do?

(A) Arrange for a skip to put it in

(B) Ensure there is a certificate of cleanliness in place before commencing work

(C) Check that the duct supports are strong enough to cope with the dismantling

(D) Make sure there are enough disc cutters to do the job

## 25.29

While using a genie hoist you notice that part of the hoist is buckling slightly. What should you do?

(A) Lower the load immediately

(B) Carry on with the job, while keeping an eye on the buckling metal

(C) Straighten out the buckled metal and then get on with the lifting operation

(D) Get the job finished quickly

## 25.30

When carrying out solvent welding on plastic ductwork, what particular safety measure **must** be applied?

(A) The area must be well ventilated

(B) The supervisor must be present

(C) A hard hat must be worn

(D) It must be done in daylight

**F**
**25**

Answers: 25.25 = D   25.26 = D   25.27 = C   25.28 = B   25.29 = A   25.30 = A        **189**

## 25.31

Which of the following do you **not** need to do before using a cleaning agent or biocide in a ductwork system?

A) Ask for advice from the cleaning agent or biocide manufacturer

B) Read the COSHH assessment for the material, carrying out a risk assessment and producing a method statement for the work

C) Consult the building occupier

D) Check what the ductwork will carry in the future

## 25.32

Which of the following do you **not** need to do before cleaning a system in industrial, laboratory or other premises where you might encounter harmful particulates?

A) Examine the system

B) Collect a sample from the ductwork

C) Run the system under overload conditions

D) Prepare a job-specific risk assessment and method statement

## 25.33

Where it is necessary to enter ductwork, which are the **two** main factors that need to be considered?

A) Working in a confined space

B) What the ductwork will carry in the future

C) The cleanliness of the ductwork

D) Whether you need to wear kneepads

E) The strength of the ductwork and its supports

## 25.34

What should you do before painting the external surface of ductwork?

A) Clean the paintbrushes

B) Read the COSHH assessment before using the paint

C) Switch off the system

D) Put on eye protection

## 25.35

What must you ensure before using a ladder?

A) That it is secured to prevent it from moving sideways or sliding outwards

B) That no-one else has booked the ladder for their work

C) That an apprentice or workmate is standing by in case you slip and fall

D) That the weather forecast is for a bright, clear day

F
25

## 25.36

When positioning and erecting a stepladder, which of the following is essential for its safe use?

- [A] It has a tool tray towards the top of the steps
- [B] The restraint mechanism is spread to its full extent
- [C] You will be able to reach the job by standing on the top step
- [D] A competent person has positioned and erected the steps

## 25.37

What is the recommended maximum height for a free-standing mobile tower?

- [A] There is no restriction
- [B] 2 m
- [C] The height recommended by the manufacturer
- [D] 12 m

## 25.38

What is the **first** thing you should do after getting on to the platform of a mobile tower?

- [A] Check that the brakes are locked on
- [B] Check the mobile tower to make sure that it has been correctly assembled
- [C] Close the access hatch to prevent falls of personnel, tools or equipment
- [D] Make sure that the tower does not rock or wobble

## 25.39

What should be done before a mobile tower is moved?

- [A] All people and equipment must be removed from the platform
- [B] A permit to work must be issued
- [C] The principal contractor must give their approval
- [D] Arrangements must be made with the forklift truck driver

## 25.40

What must be done **first** before any roof work is carried out?

- [A] A risk assessment must be carried out
- [B] The operatives working on the roof must be trained in the use of safety harnesses
- [C] Permits to work must be issued only to those allowed to work on the roof
- [D] A weather forecast must be obtained

## 25.41

What is edge protection designed to do?

- [A] Make access to the roof easier
- [B] Secure tools and materials close to the edge
- [C] Prevent rainwater running off the roof onto workers below
- [D] Prevent the fall of people and materials

**F
25**

## 25.42

When assembling a mobile tower what major overhead hazard must you be aware of?

A. Water pipes

B. Cable trays

C. False ceilings

D. Overhead service cables

## 25.43

What should folding stepladders be used for?

A. General access on site

B. Short-term works

C. All site activities where a straight ladder cannot be used

D. Getting on and off mobile towers

## 25.44

You are asked to install high-level ductwork from a platform that has no edge protection and is located above an open stairwell. What should you do?

A. Get on with the job, but keep away from the edge of the platform

B. Not start work until your work platform has been fitted with guard-rails and toe-boards

C. Get on with the job, ensuring that a workmate stays close by

D. Get on with the job, provided that if you fall the stairwell guard-rail will prevent you from falling further

## 25.45

You have been asked to install a run of ceiling-mounted ductwork across a large open-plan area, which has a good floor. What is the **best** way to access the work area?

A. From a stepladder

B. From scaffold boards and floor stands

C. By standing on packing cases

D. From mobile access towers fitted with guard-rails and toe-boards

## 25.46

You have to carry out a job over a few days on the flat roof of a two-storey building, about 1 m from the edge of the roof, which has a very low parapet. How should you reduce your risk of falling?

A. Carry on with the job, provided that you don't get dizzy with heights

B. Use a full body harness, lanyard and anchor while doing the job

C. Ask for double guard-rails and a toe-board to be installed

D. Get your mate to do the work, while you hold on to them

F
25

Answers: 25.42 = D   25.43 = B   25.44 = B   25.45 = D   25.46 = C

# 26 HVACR – RAAC Refrigeration and air conditioning

## 26.1

When a new piece of plant has been installed but has **not** been commissioned, how should it be left?

A) With all valves and switches turned off

B) With all valves and switches clearly labelled

C) With all valves and switches locked off

D) With all valves and switches turned on and ready to use

## 26.2

When working on refrigeration systems containing hydrocarbon (HC) gases, what particular danger needs to be considered?

A) There should be no sources of ignition

B) Special personal protective equipment (PPE) should be worn to prevent injuries caused by the cold

C) Extra lighting is needed to prevent trips

D) The work cannot be carried out when the weather is hot

## 26.3

What should you do when it is necessary to cut into an existing refrigerant pipe?

A) Vent the gas in the pipework to atmosphere

B) Recover the refrigerant gas and make a record of it, then do the work

C) Work on the pipework with the refrigerant gas still in it

D) Not carry out the work at all, because of the risks

## 26.4

What is the **first** thing that should be done when a new refrigeration system has been installed?

A) It should be pressure and leak tested

B) It should be filled with refrigerant

C) It should be left open to air

D) It should be turned off at the electrical switch

## 26.5

Which of these statements is true of the water in water-cooled systems?

A) It should be replaced annually

B) It should be chemically treated

C) It should be properly filtered

D) It should be drinking water

F
26

Answers: 26.1 = C   26.2 = A   26.3 = B   26.4 = A   26.5 = B

## 26.6

Who is permitted to install, service or maintain systems that contain or are designed to contain refrigerant gases?

A) A Gas Safe registered engineer

B) The person whose plant contains the gas

C) A competent, trained person who works for an F-gas registered company

D) A fully qualified electrician

## 26.7

When working in a riser, how should access be controlled?

A) By a site security operative

B) By those who are working in it

C) By the main contractor

D) By a permit to work system

## 26.8

If you find a coloured wire sticking out of an electrical plug what is the correct action to take?

A) Push it back into the plug and carry on working

B) Pull the wire clear of the plug and report it to your supervisor

C) Mark the item as defective and follow your company procedure for defective items

D) Take the plug apart and carry out a repair

## 26.9

How should extension leads in use on site be positioned?

A) They should be located so as to prevent a tripping hazard

B) They should be laid out in the shortest, most convenient route

C) They should be coiled on a drum or cable tidy

D) They should be raised on bricks

## 26.10

What should you do if you need additional temporary wiring for your power tools whilst working on site?

A) Find some cable and extend the wiring yourself

B) Stop work until an authorised supply has been installed

C) Speak to an electrician and ask them to do the temporary wiring

D) Disconnect a longer cable serving somewhere else and reconnect it to where you need it

## 26.11

Which of the following electrical equipment does **not** require portable appliance testing?

A) 110 volt electrical power tool

B) Battery-powered rechargeable power tool

C) 240 volt electrical power tool

D) 240 volt charger for battery-powered tools

F
26

## 26.12

When repairing an electrically driven compressor, what is the minimum safe method of isolation?

A Pressing the stop button

B Pressing the emergency stop button

C Turning off the local isolator

D Locking off and tagging out the local isolator

## 26.13

When a refrigerant leak is reported in a closed area, what should you do **first** before entering the area?

A Ventilate the area

B Establish that it is safe to enter

C Get a torch

D Wear safety footwear

## 26.14

Where should liquefied petroleum gas (LPG) cylinders be positioned when supplying an appliance in a site cabin?

A Inside the cabin in a locked cupboard

B Under the cabin

C Inside the cabin next to the appliance

D Outside the cabin

## 26.15

How should you position the exhaust of an engine-driven generator that has to be run inside a building?

A Outside the building

B In a stairwell

C In another room

D In a riser

## 26.16

How should cylinders (full or empty) that contain liquefied petroleum gas (LPG) or acetylene be stored on site?

A In a locked cellar with clear warning signs

B In a locked cage at least 3 m from any oxygen cylinders

C As close to the point of use as possible

D Covered by a tarpaulin to shield the compressed cylinder from sunlight

## 26.17

You spill some oil on the floor and you do not have any absorbent material to clean the area. What should you do?

A Spread it about to lessen the depth

B Keep people out of the area and inform your supervisor

C Do nothing, it will eventually soak into the floor

D Warn other people as they tread through it

F
26

### 26.18

Which is the safest place to store refrigerant cylinders when they are **not** in use?

A. Outside in a special locked storage compound

B. In a company vehicle

C. Inside the building in a locked cupboard

D. In the immediate work area, ready for use the next day

### 26.19

If refrigerant gases are released into a closed room in a building, what would they do?

A. Sink to the floor

B. Rise to the ceiling

C. Stay at the same level

D. Disperse safely within the room

### 26.20

You have to drill through a wall panel that you suspect contains an asbestos material. What should you do?

A. Ignore it and carry on

B. Put on safety goggles

C. Put on a dust mask

D. Stop work and report it

### 26.21

When using a van to transport a refrigerant bottle, how should it be carried?

A. In the back of the van

B. In the passenger footwell of the van

C. In a purpose-built container within the rear of the van, with appropriate signage

D. In the van with all the windows open

### 26.22

What safety devices should be fitted between the pipes and the gauges of oxy-propane brazing equipment?

A. Non-return valves

B. On-off taps

C. Flame retardant tape

D. Flashback arresters

### 26.23

Why is it essential to take great care when handling oxygen cylinders?

A. They contain highly flammable compressed gas

B. They contain highly flammable liquid gas

C. They are filled to extremely high pressures

D. They contain poisonous gas

F
26

## 26.24

What part of your body could suffer long-term damage when you hand-bend copper pipe using a spring?

[A] Elbows

[B] Shoulders

[C] Back

[D] Knees

## 26.25

If you are working where welding is being carried out, what should be provided to protect you from welding flash?

[A] Fire extinguishers

[B] Warning notices

[C] Screens

[D] Hi-vis vest

## 26.26

When using a blowtorch or brazing equipment to joint copper tube and fittings in a property, how should a fire extinguisher be made available?

[A] It should be available in the immediate work area

[B] It should be held over the joint while you are using the blowtorch

[C] It should be used to cool the fitting

[D] It should be available only if a property is occupied

## 26.27

When should you stop using a blowtorch or brazing equipment?

[A] Immediately before leaving the job

[B] At least one hour before leaving the job

[C] At least two hours before leaving the job

[D] At least four hours before leaving the job

## 26.28

Why must you **never** use oxygen when pressure testing?

[A] The molecules of the gas are too small

[B] The pressure required would not be reached

[C] When oxygen meets oil in a compressor it could explode and cause serious injury or death

[D] There is too much temperature pressure difference and a true record will not be given

## 26.29

What should you ensure when pressure testing with nitrogen?

[A] That the nitrogen bottle is laid down to avoid it falling over

[B] That the nitrogen gauge can take the pressure required and that the bottle is secured upright

[C] That the temperature of the bottle is at room temperature to avoid a temperature pressure difference

[D] That purge brazing has taken place during the installation

F
26

Answers: 26.24 = D   26.25 = C   26.26 = A   26.27 = B   26.28 = C   26.29 = B

## 26.30

When planning a lifting operation how should the sequence of operations to enable a safe lift be confirmed?

A  By verbal instruction

B  In a method statement

C  In a radio telephone message

D  Via a notice in the canteen

## 26.31

Which of these statements is true in relation to the SWL of lifting equipment?

A  It is never marked on the equipment but kept with the test certificates

B  It is provided for guidance only

C  It may be exceeded by no more than 25%

D  It is the absolute maximum safe working load

## 26.32

What must be clearly marked on all lifting equipment?

A  The name of the manufacturer

B  The safe working load

C  The next test date

D  The specification of material from which it is made

## 26.33

What particular item of personal protective equipment (PPE) should you use when oxyacetylene brazing?

A  Ear defenders

B  Clear goggles

C  Green-tinted goggles

D  Dust mask

## 26.34

How should you position the bottles when using oxyacetylene brazing equipment?

A  Laid on their side

B  Stood upright and secured

C  Stood upside down

D  Angled at 45°

## 26.35

Which **two** of the following are essential safety checks that need to be carried out before using oxyacetylene equipment?

A  That the cylinders are full

B  That the cylinders, hoses and flashback arresters are in good condition

C  That the trolley wheels are the right size

D  That the area is well ventilated and clear of any obstructions

E  That the cylinders are the right weight

F
26

Answers: 26.30 = B   26.31 = D   26.32 = B   26.33 = C   26.34 = B   26.35 = B, D

## 26.36

When handling refrigerant gases, what personal protective equipment (PPE) should you wear as a minimum?

A) Eye protection, overalls, thermal-resistant gloves and helmet

B) Eye protection, overalls, thermal-resistant gloves and safety boots

C) Eye protection, overalls, harness and safety boots

D) Overalls, thermal-resistant gloves, helmet and safety boots

## 26.37

What should you establish before entering a cold room?

A) The size of the cold room

B) The temperature of the cold room

C) Whether the exit door is fitted with an internal handle

D) Whether there are lights and power in the cold room

## 26.38

What must you ensure before using a ladder?

A) That it is secured to prevent it from moving sideways or sliding outwards

B) That no-one else has booked the ladder for their work

C) That an apprentice or workmate is standing by in case you slip and fall

D) That the weather forecast is for a bright, clear day

## 26.39

When positioning and erecting a stepladder, which of the following is essential for its safe use?

A) It has a tool tray towards the top of the steps

B) The restraint mechanism is spread to its full extent

C) You will be able to reach the job by standing on the top step

D) A competent person has positioned and erected the steps

## 26.40

What is the recommended maximum height for a free-standing mobile tower?

A) There is no restriction

B) 2 m

C) The height recommended by the manufacturer

D) 12 m

## 26.41

What is the **first** thing you should do after getting on to the platform of a mobile tower?

A) Check that the brakes are locked on

B) Check the mobile tower to make sure that it has been correctly assembled

C) Close the access hatch to prevent falls of personnel, tools or equipment

D) Make sure that the tower does not rock or wobble

F
26

## 26.42

What should be done before a mobile tower is moved?

- A All people and equipment must be removed from the platform
- B A permit to work must be issued
- C The principal contractor must give their approval
- D Arrangements must be made with the forklift truck driver

## 26.43

What must be done **first** before any roof work is carried out?

- A A risk assessment must be carried out
- B The operatives working on the roof must be trained in the use of safety harnesses
- C Permits to work must be issued only to those allowed to work on the roof
- D A weather forecast must be obtained

## 26.44

What is edge protection designed to do?

- A Make access to the roof easier
- B Secure tools and materials close to the edge
- C Prevent rainwater running off the roof onto workers below
- D Prevent the fall of people and materials

## 26.45

What is the **first** thing you should do after getting on to the platform of a correctly erected mobile tower?

- A Check that the brakes are locked on
- B Check the mobile tower to make sure that it has been correctly assembled
- C Close the access hatch to prevent falls of personnel, tools or equipment
- D Make sure that the tower does not rock or wobble

## 26.46

When assembling a mobile tower what major overhead hazard **must** you be aware of?

- A Water pipes
- B Cable trays
- C False ceilings
- D Overhead service cables

## 26.47

What should folding stepladders be used for?

- A General access on site
- B Short-term work
- C All site activities where a straight ladder cannot be used
- D Getting on and off mobile towers

F
26

## 26.48

You have to carry out a job, over a few days, on the flat roof of a two-storey building, about 1 m from the edge of the roof, which has a very low parapet. How should you reduce your risk of falling?

A Carry on with the job, provided you don't get dizzy with heights

B Use a full body harness, lanyard and anchor while doing the job

C Ask for double guard-rails and toe-boards to be installed to prevent you falling

D Get your mate to do the work, while you hold on to them

## 26.49

You have been asked to install a number of ceiling-mounted air-conditioning units in a large open-plan area, which has a good floor. What is the **best** way to access the work area?

A From a stepladder

B From scaffold boards and floor stands

C By standing on packing cases

D From a mobile tower

F
26

# 27 HVACR – SAF Services and facilities maintenance

## 27.1

When arriving at an occupied building, who or what should you consult to find out about any asbestos in the premises before starting work?

A. The person responsible for the building, so you can view the asbestos register

B. The building's receptionist

C. The building's logbook

D. The building's caretaker

## 27.2

Where might you find information on the safe way to maintain the services in a building?

A. The noticeboard

B. The safety officer

C. The local Health and Safety Executive (HSE) office

D. The health and safety file for the building

## 27.3

In the normal office environment what should be the hot water temperature at the tap furthest from the boiler, after it has been run for one minute?

A. At least 15°C

B. At least 35°C

C. At least 50°C

D. At least 100°C

## 27.4

What should be the maximum temperature for a cold water supply, after it has been run for one minute?

A. 10°C

B. 20°C

C. 35°C

D. 50°C

## 27.5

What is required if there is a cooling tower on site?

A. A formal logbook

B. A written scheme of examination

C. Regular visits by the local authority environmental health officer

D. Inspections by the water supplier

## 27.6

Which **two** of the following are pressure systems?

A. Medium and high temperature hot water systems at or above 95°C

B. Cold water systems

C. Steam systems

D. Office tea urns

E. Domestic heating systems

F
27

Answers: 27.1 = A   27.2 = D   27.3 = C   27.4 = B   27.5 = A   27.6 = A, C

## 27.7

What is required before a pressure system can be operated?

A. A written scheme of examination

B. A permit to work

C. City & Guilds certification

D. A minimum of two competent persons to operate the system

## 27.8

Which of these statements is **true** in relation to the water used in cooling systems?

A. It should be replaced annually

B. It should be chemically treated

C. It should be chilled

D. It should be drinking water

## 27.9

Which of the following should you **not** do when replacing the filters in an air-conditioning system?

A. Put the old filters in a dustbin

B. Follow a job-specific risk assessment and method statement

C. Wear appropriate overalls

D. Wear a respirator

## 27.10

After servicing a gas boiler what checks must you make by law?

A. Check for water leaks

B. Check for flueing, ventilation, gas rate and safe functioning

C. Check the pressure relief valve

D. Check the thermostat setting

## 27.11

What **must** you do before adding inhibitor to a heating system?

A. Check for leaks on the system

B. Raise the system to working temperature

C. Read the COSHH assessment for the product

D. Bleed the heat emitters

## 27.12

How should access to a riser be controlled?

A. By a site security operative

B. By those who are working in it

C. By the main contractor

D. By a permit to work system

F
27

Answers: 27.7 = A   27.8 = B   27.9 = A   27.10 = B   27.11 = C   27.12 = D

## 27.13

What is the correct action to take if natural gas is detected in an underground service duct?

[A] No action, it is not harmful

[B] Evacuate the duct

[C] Carry on working but do not use electrical equipment

[D] Carry on working until the end of the shift

## 27.14

What should you consider **first** when planning to work in a confined space?

[A] Whether the job has been priced properly

[B] Whether sufficient manpower has been allocated

[C] Whether the correct tools have been arranged

[D] Whether the work could be done in another way to avoid the need to enter the confined space

## 27.15

How should an adequate supply of breathable fresh air be provided in a confined space when breathing equipment is **not** being worn?

[A] An opening in the top of the confined space

[B] Forced mechanical ventilation

[C] Natural ventilation

[D] An opening at the bottom of the confined space

## 27.16

What are the **two** main safety considerations when using oxyacetylene equipment in a confined space?

[A] The hoses may not be long enough

[B] Unburnt oxygen may cause an oxygen-enriched atmosphere

[C] The burner will be hard to light

[D] Wearing the correct goggles

[E] The risk of a flammable gas leak

## 27.17

What precaution should be taken to protect against lighting failure in a confined space?

[A] Remember where you got in

[B] Ensure it is daylight when you do the work

[C] Each operative should carry a torch

[D] Secure a rope near the entrance and trail it behind you so that you can trace your way back

F
27

## 27.18

While working on your own and tracing pipework in a building, you notice that the pipes enter a service duct. What should you do?

A  Go into the service duct and continue to trace the pipework

B  Ask someone in the building to act as your second person

C  Put on your personal protective equipment (PPE) and carry on with the job

D  Stop work until a risk assessment has been carried out

## 27.19

Before working on electrically powered equipment, what is the procedure to make sure that the supply is dead before work starts?

A  Switch off and remove the fuses

B  Switch off and cut through the supply with insulated pliers

C  Test the circuit, switch off and isolate the supply at the mains board

D  Switch off, isolate the supply at the mains board, lock and tag out

## 27.20

When you are about to work on electrical equipment and the main isolator does **not** have a lock-out device, what is an alternative method of isolating the supply?

A  Detach the mains power supply

B  Place insulating material in the contactors

C  There is no alternative to a lock-out device for isolating the supply

D  Withdraw and retain the fuse and post notices warning that the machinery is being worked on

## 27.21

What would you use to find out whether a wall into which you are about to drill contains an electric supply?

A  A neon screwdriver

B  A cable tracer

C  A multimeter

D  A hammer and chisel

## 27.22

Which type of power drill is most suitable for fixing a run of pipework outside in wet weather?

A  Battery-powered drill

B  Drill with 110 volt power supply

C  Drill with 24 volt power supply

D  Any mains voltage drill with a power breaker

F
27

Answers: 27.18 = D   27.19 = D   27.20 = D   27.21 = B   27.22 = A

## 27.23

Why is temporary continuity bonding carried out before removing and replacing sections of metallic pipework?

A To provide a continuous earth for the pipework installation

B To prevent any chance of blowing a fuse

C To maintain the live supply to the electrical circuit

D To prevent any chance of corrosion to the pipework

## 27.24

What is the procedure for ensuring that the electrical supply is dead before replacing an electric immersion heater?

A Switch off and disconnect the supply to the immersion heater

B Switch off and cut through the electric cable with insulated pliers

C Switch off and test the circuit

D Lock off the supply, isolate at the mains board, test the circuit and hang a warning sign

## 27.25

What is used to reduce 230 volts to 110 volts on site?

A RCD (residual current device)

B Transformer

C Circuit breaker

D Step-down generator

## 27.26

What colour power outlet on a portable generator would supply 230 volts?

A Black

B Blue

C Red

D Yellow

## 27.27

What action should you take if a natural gas leak is reported in a closed area?

A Ventilate the area and phone the gas emergency service

B Establish whether or not it is safe to enter

C Turn off the light

D Wear safety footwear

## 27.28

Which of the following **two** actions should you take if a refrigerant leak is reported in a closed area?

A Ventilate the area and extinguish all naked flames

B Trace the leak and make a temporary repair

C Establish whether or not it is safe to enter

D Switch off the system

E No action required as refrigerant gas is harmless

F
27

Answers: 27.23 = A   27.24 = D   27.25 = B   27.26 = B   27.27 = A   27.28 = A, C

**27.29**

How is legionella transmitted?

A By breathing contaminated airborne water droplets

B Through human contact

C Through contact with dirty clothes

D Via rat urine

**27.30**

What is the ideal temperature for legionella to breed?

A Below 20°C

B Between 20°C and 45°C

C Between 45°C and 75°C

D Between 75°C and 100°C

**27.31**

Which of the following is the most likely place to find legionella?

A In drinking water

B In hot water taps above 50°C

C In infrequently used shower heads

D In a river

**27.32**

When assembling a mobile access tower what major overhead hazard must you be aware of?

A Water pipes

B Cable trays

C False ceilings

D Overhead service cables

**27.33**

You spill some oil on the floor and you do **not** have any absorbent material to clean the area. What should you do?

A Spread it about to lessen the depth

B Keep people out of the area and inform your supervisor

C Do nothing, it will eventually soak into the floor

D Warn other people as they tread through it

**27.34**

How should liquefied petroleum gas (LPG) cylinders be carried to and from premises in a van?

A In the back of the van

B In the passenger footwell of the van

C In a purpose-built container within the rear of the van, with appropriate signage

D In the van with all the windows open

F
27

Answers: 27.29 = A   27.30 = B   27.31 = C   27.32 = D   27.33 = B   27.34 = C

### 27.35

When removing some panelling, you see a section of cabling with the wires showing. What should you do?

A  Carry on with your work, trying your best to avoid the cables

B  Touch the cables to see if they are live, and if so refuse to carry out the work

C  Wrap the defective cable with approved electrical insulation tape

D  Only work when the cable has been isolated or repaired by a competent person

### 27.36

When **must** a shaft or pit be securely covered or have double guard-rails and toe-boards installed?

A  At a fall height of 1 m

B  When there is a potential risk of anyone falling into it

C  At a fall height of 2.5 m

D  At a fall height of 3 m

### 27.37

What should you do if, when carrying out a particular task, the correct tool is **not** available?

A  Wait until you have the appropriate tool for the task

B  Borrow a tool from the building caretaker

C  Use the best tool available in the toolkit

D  Modify one of the tools you have

### 27.38

Who should be informed if a legionella outbreak is suspected?

A  The Health and Safety Executive (HSE)

B  The police

C  A coroner

D  The nearest hospital

### 27.39

When should the use of a permit to work be considered?

A  For all high risk work activities

B  For all equipment isolations

C  At the beginning of each shift

D  When there is enough time to complete the paperwork

### 27.40

Who should fit a padlock and tag to an electrical lock-out guard?

A  Anyone working on the unit

B  The engineer who fitted the lock-out device

C  The senior engineer

D  Anyone

F
27

## 27.41

You arrive on site and find the mains isolator for a component is switched off. What should you do?

A Switch it on and get on with your work

B Switch it on and check the safety circuits to see if there is a fault

C Contact the person in control of the premises

D Ask people around the building and if no-one responds, switch it on and get on with your work

## 27.42

When carrying out solvent welding on plastic pipework, what particular safety measure **must** you apply?

A The area must be well ventilated

B The supervisor must be present

C The area must be enclosed

D It must be done in daylight

## 27.43

Before starting work on a particular piece of equipment, who or what should you consult?

A The machine brochure

B The operation and maintenance manual for the equipment

C The manufacturer's data plate

D The store person

## 27.44

Which **two** of the following should a person who is going to work alone carry out to ensure their safety?

A Register their presence with the site representative before starting work

B Ensure their timesheet is accurate and countersigned

C Make sure that somebody regularly checks that they are OK

D Notify the site manager of the details of the work

E Only work outside of normal working hours

## 27.45

What must you ensure to prevent unauthorised access to an unoccupied plant or switchgear room?

A That the access door is locked

B That a sign is posted

C That the power supply is isolated

D That a person is posted to prevent access

## 27.46

What should folding stepladders be used for?

A General access on site

B Short-term work

C All work at height where a straight ladder cannot be used

D Getting on and off mobile towers

F
27

Answers: 27.41 = C   27.42 = A   27.43 = B   27.44 = A, C   27.45 = A   27.46 = B   **209**

## 27.47

When positioning and erecting a stepladder, which of the following is essential for its safe use?

A. It has a tool tray towards the top of the steps

B. The restraint mechanism is spread to its full extent

C. You will be able to reach the job by standing on the top step

D. A competent person has positioned and erected the steps

## 27.48

What is the **first** thing you should do after getting onto the platform of a correctly erected mobile tower?

A. Check that the brakes are locked on

B. Check the mobile tower to make sure that it has been correctly assembled

C. Close the access hatch to prevent falls of personnel, tools or equipment

D. Make sure that the tower does not rock or wobble

## 27.49

Before using a ladder at work, you notice that the maker's label says that it is a Class 3 ladder. What does this mean?

A. It is for domestic use only and must not be used in connection with work

B. It is of industrial quality and can be used safely

C. It has been made to a European Standard

D. It is made of insulating material and can be used near to overhead cables

F
27

# Further information

**Contents**

## Preparing for the case studies

Construction is an exciting industry. There is constant change as work progresses to completion.

As a result, the construction site is one of the most dangerous environments to work in.

Everyone on site working together can avoid many of the accidents that happen. The free film *Setting out* shows what you and the site must do to stay healthy and safe at work.

To watch the film:

 go online at *www.citb.co.uk/settingout*.

This film is essential viewing for everyone involved in construction, and should be viewed before sitting the CITB *Health, safety and environment test*.

The content of the film is summarised here. These principles form the basis for the behavioural case studies.

*It is advisable to watch the film. However, for those unable to view it or who want to refresh themselves on the content, the full transcript is provided for your information.*

### Part 1: What you should expect from the construction industry

Your site and your employer should be doing all they can to keep you and your colleagues safe.

Before any work begins, the site management team will have been planning and preparing the site for your arrival. It's their job to ensure that you can do your job safely and efficiently.

**Five things the site you are working on must do:**
- ☑ know when you are on site
- ☑ give you a site induction
- ☑ give you site-specific information
- ☑ encourage communication
- ☑ keep you up to date and informed.

### Part 2: What the industry expects of you

Once the work begins, it's up to every individual to take responsibility for carrying out the plan safely.

This means you should follow the rules and guidelines as well as being alert to the continuing changes on site.

**Five things you must do:**
- ☑ respect and follow the site rules
- ☑ safely prepare each task
- ☑ carry out each task responsibly
- ☑ know when to stop (if you think anything is unsafe)
- ☑ keep learning.

# Setting out – the transcript

**What to expect from the industry and what the industry expects from you**

Construction is an exciting industry. There is constant change as work progresses to completion.

As a result, the construction site is one of the most dangerous environments to work in.

Many accidents that occur on sites can be avoided. In this film you will find out what you and the site must do to stay healthy and safe at work.

## Part 1: What to expect from the industry

When you arrive for your first day on a site, it will not be the first day for everyone.

Before any work begins, the site management team will have been planning and preparing the site for your arrival.

It is *their* job to ensure that you can do *your* job safely and efficiently.

So what are five key things the site should do for you?

### 1. Your site must know when you are on site

When you arrive you should be greeted and welcomed by someone on site. If you are not then make your presence known to site management.

You need to know who is in charge and they need to know who is working on, or visiting, their site.

You may be asked to sign in or report to someone in charge when you arrive. You should also sign out or let someone know if you are leaving.

### 2. Your site must give you an induction

Once you have introduced yourself, you will be given a site induction. This is a legal requirement to give you basic information so that you can work safely on site.

You may be asked to watch a video or look at a presentation. It is important that you understand what is said during the induction. If there is something you are not sure about, don't be afraid to ask for more information. If you have not been to the site for a while, you need to be sure that you are up to date. Check with site management whether you need a briefing or a further induction.

## 3. Your site must give you site-specific information

Whether you are just starting out or have decades of experience, every job is different. So it is very important that the site induction is specific to your site.

You should be told about any specific areas of danger and what site rules are in place to control these.

You will be told who the managers are on site and what arrangements are in place for emergencies.

You will also find out what to do it there is a fire or if you need to sound an alarm.

It may sound basic, but there must be good welfare facilities.

You must also be able to take a break somewhere that is warm and dry.

## 4. Your site must encourage communication

Evidence shows that there are fewer incidents and accidents on sites where workers are actively involved in health and safety. Your opinions and ideas are important so make them heard.

Whatever the size of your site there should be many opportunities to do this. For example, directly with managers through a daily briefing or through suggestion boxes. Managers should let you know how best to do this on your site.

## 5. Your site must keep you up to date

Construction sites are constantly changing and unplanned activities can be a major cause of accidents. The more up to date you are about what is happening on site, the more you can understand the dangers. The best sites keep their people informed on daily activities.

Is there a hazards board on your site – is it regularly updated?

Your site management should be telling you what's going on, on a regular basis.

**Your site should be doing all it can to keep you and your colleagues safe. If it is not – say something and work together to make it better.**

## Part 2: What the industry expects from you

Site management will have planned ahead to make work on site as safe as possible for you. Once the work begins, it is up to every individual to take responsibility for carrying out the plan safely. This means following the guidelines set out and being alert to the continuing changes on site.

So what will the site expect from you?

### 1. You must respect site rules

Site rules are there to minimise the risk of particularly hazardous activities, such as moving vehicles and handling flammable substances.

Moving traffic on site is a major cause of accidents. Often rules will cover issues like walking through the site, where to park, and how to behave when you see a moving vehicle.

They may also tell you where you can smoke and remind you to tidy equipment away when it is not in use.

These might feel restrictive but they have been put in place for a reason. If that reason is not clear to you, ask for more information. Otherwise, follow the rules to stay safe.

### 2. You must safely prepare each task

Every task carried out on site is unique and will have its own dangers, for instance working at height or manual handling. The site management team will put in place a plan to avoid or minimise the dangers before the start of work. The plan may be written down in a risk assessment, a method statement or a task sheet.

This will tell you what to do, the skills needed, what to wear, what tools to use and what the dangers are.

You should contribute to the planning process using your experience and knowledge.

For example, before working at height, which is a high-risk activity, you must consider:

☑ Is the access suitable for what you need to do?

☑ Do you have the right tools?

☑ Do you have the right protective equipment, does it fit, and is it comfortable?

### 3. You must do each task responsibly

Once you are at work you must apply your training, skills and common sense to your tasks at all times.

For example, if you are building a wall, you may have to move heavy loads. But you must not put your health and body in danger. Make sure you move the load as safely as possible, as you should have been trained to do. And if you are not sure how to, then you must ask for advice.

Equally, it is important to be aware of the dangers to those around you. For example, if someone working with you is not wearing the correct PPE for a certain activity, tell them so.

Acting responsibly will benefit both you and your colleagues.

### 4. You must know when to stop

In our industry saying NO is not easy. We are fixers and doers. We CAN do.

However, a significant number of accidents on sites happen when people are doing things that they're not comfortable with.

For example, many workers have been harmed by not knowing how to identify asbestos. If you think there is any likelihood that there is asbestos present where you are working, you must stop work and seek advice.

If you are not properly trained, equipped, or briefed – or if the situation around you changes – the result could be an accident.

Trust your instincts. If things feel beyond your control or dangerous or, if you see someone else working unsafely, stop the work immediately and inform site management why you have done so.

You might prevent an injury or save a life. Your employer should be supportive if you do this because you have the right to say no and the responsibility to not walk by.

### 5. You must keep learning

If your job requires you to have specific training to enable you to do it safely then it is your employer's responsibility to provide it.

To really get the best out of your career, you should keep learning about developments in machinery, equipment, regulations and training.

This will not only give you greater confidence and understanding, it will ensure you remain healthy and safe.

### In summary

Construction is so much more than bricks and mortar. The work we do improves the world around us. It's time for us to work together to build a safer and better industry.

# Acknowledgements

**CITB wishes to acknowledge the assistance offered by the following organisations in the preparation of the question banks:**

- ☑ Association of Technical Lightning & Access Specialists (ATLAS)
- ☑ Building & Engineering Services Association (B&ES)
- ☑ CECA (Environmental)
- ☑ Civil Engineering Contractors Association (CECA)
- ☑ Construction Plant-hire Association
- ☑ Environment Agency
- ☑ Green Construction Board
- ☑ Health & Safety Executive (HSE)
- ☑ LANTRA – National Training Organisation for the Land Based Industries
- ☑ Lift and Escalator Industry Association (LEIA)
- ☑ National Access and Scaffolding Confederation (NASC)
- ☑ National Federation of Demolition Contractors
- ☑ UK Contractors Group (UKCG)
- ☑ Union of Construction, Allied Trades and Technicians (UCATT)
- ☑ Unite the Union

Notes